Sounds of Our HERITAGE

from the Pacific

BILL MARTIN, JR.
General Editor

BERNARD J. WEISS
Senior Author, Holt Basic Reading

Holt, Rinehart and Winston, Publishers
New York • Toronto • London • Sydney

Acknowledgments

The authors and Holt, Rinehart and Winston, Publishers, thank the following publishers, authors, agents, and parties whose help and permission to reprint materials have made this book possible. If any errors in acknowledgments have occurred, the errors were inadvertent and will be corrected in subsequent editions as they are realized.

AMS Press for excerpted adapted selection "Lucky Strike" from *Western Folklore XV: 4* collected by Henry Winfred Splitter. Copyright © 1956. Used by permission.

Atheneum Publishers for "Onto a Boy's Arm Came a Mosquito" from *Songs of the Dream People: Chants and Images from the Indians and Eskimos of North America* edited by James Houston (A Margaret K. McElderry Book). Copyright © 1972 by James Houston. Used by permission.

The Caxton Printers, Ltd., Caldwell, Idaho, for "Paul Digs Puget Sound" from *Tall Timber Tales* by Dell J. McCormick. Used by permission.

M. M. Cole Publishing Company for "Lumberjack's Alphabet" by Elmore Vincent. Used by permission.

Dell Publishing Company for "Papago Indian Chant (The Edge of the World)" from *The Tree Stands Shining,* poems collected by Hettie Jones. Used by permission.

The Dial Press for adaptation of "Maria's Adventures in New Spain" from the book *As I Saw It; Women Who Lived the American Adventure* by Cheryl G. Hoople. Copyright © 1978 by Cheryl G. Hoople. Used by permission.

Dodd, Mead & Company, Inc. for adaptation of "The Loon's Necklace" and "The Coming of the Salmon" from *Indian Adventure Tales* by Allen A. MacFarlan. Copyright © 1955 by Allan A. MacFarlan. For excerpted adapted selection "The Mystery of Bigfoot" from *The Greatest Monster in the World* by Daniel Cohen. Copyright © 1975 by Daniel Cohen. Used by permission.

Follett Publishing Company (division of Follett Corporation), for "Coming to America: Miki Akiyama Uchida's Story" excerpted from *Tales of the Elders* collected by Carol Ann Bales. Copyright © 1977 by Carol Ann Bales. Used by permission.

Houghton Mifflin Company for "The Mansion of the Dead" excerpted and adapted from *The Haunting of America* by Jean Anderson. Copyright © 1973 by Helen Jean Anderson. Used by permission.

Indiana University Press for excerpted adapted selection "Hathaway Jones and the Flying Bear" from *Tall Tales from Rogue River* edited by Stephen Dow Beckham. Used by permission.

Island Heritage Books, Honolulu, Hawaii, for "Felisa and the Tikling Bird" adapted and excerpted from *Felisa and the Tikling Bird* by Jodi Parry Belknap. Copyright © 1973 by Island Heritage Books. Used by permission.

Alfred A. Knopf, Inc., for adaptation of "Paul Digs Puget Sound" by Dell J. McCormick and "Puget Sound" a poem by Harold W. Felton from *Legends of Paul Bunyan* compiled and edited by Harold W. Felton. Copyright 1947 by Alfred A. Knopf, Inc. Renewed © 1975 by Harold W. Felton. For adaptation of "Lazy Coyote," from *An Everyday History of Somewhere* by Ray Raphael. Copyright © 1974 by Ray Raphael. Used by permission.

J. B. Lippincott Company for "Agayk and the Strangest Spear" excerpted and adapted from *Trickster Tales* by I. G. Edmonds. Copyright © 1966 by G. I. Edmonds. Used by permission.

National Geographic School Bulletin (Nepal) for excerpted adapted selection "The Mystery of Bigfoot" from "The Old Explorer" 9/17/73. Used by permission.

The Oregon Historical Society and The Champoeg Press for "Woods Words" from *A Comprehensive Dictionary of Loggers Tales* by Walter F. McCulloch. Copyright © 1958. Used by permission.

Philomel Books for Eskimo poem "Footprints" from collection of poems *Beyond the High Hills* by Knud Rasmussen. Copyright © 1961 by The World Publishing Company. Used by permission.

Plays, Inc., for adaptation of *Sourdough Sally,* a play by Helen Louise Walker. Reprinted from *Easy Plays for Boys and Girls* by Helen Louise Miller. Copyright © 1963 by Plays, Inc. This play is for reading purposes only. For permission to produce this play, write Plays, Inc., 8 Arlington St., Boston, MA 02116. Used by permission.

J. A. Rickard for excerpted adaptation of "Palomo and Felipe" from *The Old Aztec Storyteller* by J. A. Rickard. Copyright 1944 by J. A. Rickard. Used by permission.

Macrae Smith for excerpted adapted selection "Tangling with a Grizzly," from *Black Courage* by A. E. Schraff. Used by permission.

University of Oregon for excerpted adapted selections "Helmer Lindstrom: Fisherman and Boat Carpenter," "Benjamin Franklin Finn," and "Lumberjack Lore," from *Northwest Folklore, Vol. II No. 1* edited by Suzi Jones. For "The Blue Bucket Mine" from

Gold and Cattle Country by Herman Oliver. Used by permission.

Kenneth Williams for excerpted adapted selection "The Ghostly Hitchiker. Used by permission.

Yale University Press for excerpted adapted selection "A Frontier Lady' (Sarah Royce: Diary of a Pioneer Woman)" from *Recollections of the Gold Rush and Early California* by Sarah Royce. Copyright © 1962 by Yale University Press. Used by permission.

Any material on evolution presented in this book is presented as theory rather than fact.

Photo Credits

COVER: (right) "San Francisco, 1841" by George Henry Burgress, The Oakland Museum; (top left) Shostal Associates; (bottom left) ©Harald Sund/The Image Bank.

UNIT 1: pp.8–9 Library of Congress; p.10 (top) Propix/Monkmeyer Press Photo, (bottom) Hawaii Visitors' Bureau; p.11 (top) Zelenka/Monkmeyer Press Photo, (bottom) Jay Lurie; p.12 (top) Union Pacific Railroad, (bottom) Frank Siteman/Stock, Boston; p.13 (top) Propix/Monkmeyer Press Photos, (bottom) Alexander Lowry/Photo Researchers; p.14 (top) ©Steve Maslowski/Photo Researchers, (bottom right) Jen & Less Bartlett/Photo Researchers, (bottom left) Photo Researchers; p.15 ©Tom McHugh 1977/Photo Researchers; p.33 Carol Bates.

UNIT 2: pp.50–1 Steve McCutcheon/Alaska Pictorial Service; p.62 United Press International; p.64 (top) Photograph Coll. Suzallo Library, University of Washington, (bottom right) Union Pacific Railroad, (bottom left) Bettmann Archive; p.65 (top) San Diego Historical Society, (middle) ©Leonard Lee Rue III/Photo Researchers, (bottom)

Art Credits

TABLE OF CONTENTS

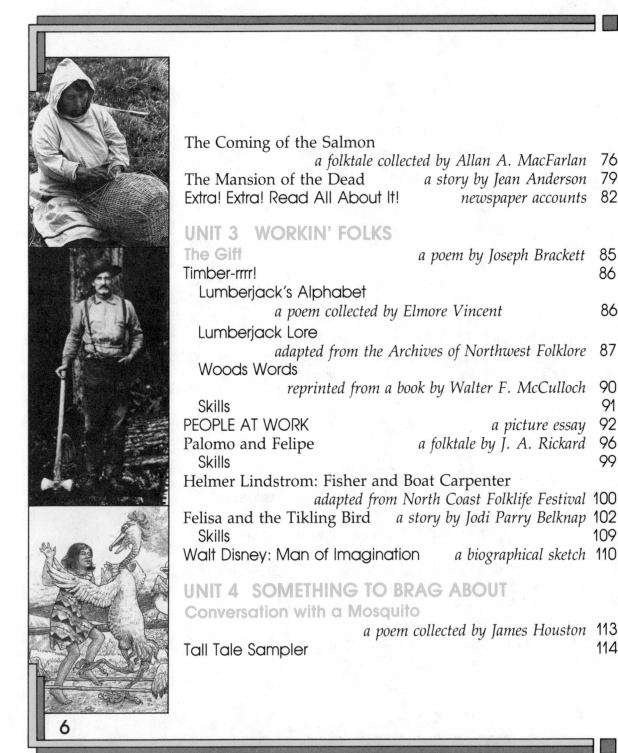

ROADS TO RICHES

The Edge of the World

At the edge of the world
It is growing light.
The trees stand shining.
I like it.
It is growing light.

collected by Hettie Jones

Pacific States: Land of Contrasts

The Pacific States are amazing! Imagine mountains, valleys, sandy beaches, and surf. Dream of forests, rain forests, deserts, volcanoes, hot springs, geysers, iceburgs, and lava beds! It's all here.

Colony Glacier near Palmer, Alaska

Lumahai Beach, Hawaii

Big Sur, California

It's a land of contrasts. Alaska has thousands of glaciers. Malaspina, North America's largest glacier, is almost fifty miles wide. In Oregon you can find the largest lava beds. And in Hawaii, volcanoes such as Mauna Loa and Kilauea are still active. Mt. St. Helens, in Washington, blew its top in recent times.

The great Pacific States stretch thousands of miles from California to Oregon to Washington to Alaska to Hawaii. All five states border on the Pacific Ocean.

Coast of Oregon

Warm tides, rain, and sunshine have made these states a giant food basket. Grapes, peaches, plums, figs, apricots, oranges, and strawberries from California. Apples, cherries, peaches, and pears from Oregon and Washington. Pineapples, mangoes, bananas, guava, lilikai, and papayas from Hawaii. Almonds, walnuts, artichokes, lettuce . . . Oh, what bounty!

California grows one-third of all the fruit in the United States. But fruit grows faster in Alaska than in California. Why? Because the summer sun shines there twenty hours a day!

Listen to Dick Gratiot brag about Alaskan fruit. "I raised a strawberry up here last summer," said Dick. "A guy stopped and wanted a quart of strawberries. I told him I wouldn't cut *a* strawberry for anybody."

Washington rain forest

Fruit and vegetable market

Even mountains are higher in the Pacific States. Do you want to see the highest place in North America? Hop a plane for Mt. McKinley in Alaska. Death Valley in California is the lowest point in the United States.

Mount McKinley, Alaska

Things just naturally grow bigger in the Pacific States. California's General Sherman Sequoia is the largest living plant in the world. It's 275 feet tall and 85 feet around! California redwoods grow taller still—up to 365 feet high.

Death Valley, California

Polar bear

Would you like to go on a safari? Visit the Pacific States. Picture forests filled with black bears, elk, deer, wild goats, even jumping mice. Further north, you'll see seals, polar bears, whales, moose, caribou, arctic foxes, and lots of bears. And in Hawaii are mongooses and dolphins.

Caribou

Dolphins

This is the place for fishers too. Fish for shrimp, crab, salmon, trout, and bass. Sink a line for perch, tuna, anchovies, halibut, and herring. Watch out for sharks!

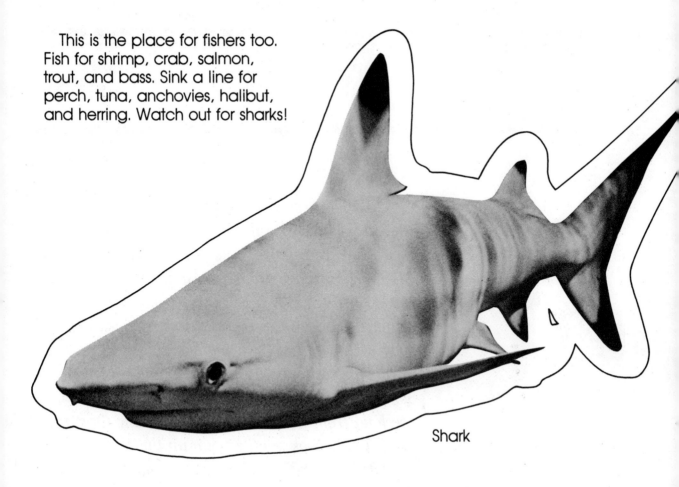

Shark

Take a trip *now* to the Pacific States. Imagine this land as it was and see it as it is today. Listen to the tales Indians told their children. Learn about the settlers from the East and their dreams. Relive the adventure of the gold rush. Dream about the excitement of the pioneers. It's all here in the legends, myths, tales, history, pictures, and fantasy.

GOLD FEVER

prospector
(pros' pek tər)
person who
explores a region
searching for
gold, silver, oil,
uranium, etc.

nugget
(nug' it)
valuable lump

"Gold has been discovered in California!" In 1848 this news spread with lightning speed all over the eastern part of the United States. In 1849, California's population jumped from 26,000 to 115,000. Immigrants from Australia, China, Ireland, France, and Mexico joined the flood of Americans from the East. They traveled in covered wagons, on horseback, and on foot. Some went in ships to Panama, then crossed overland from the Atlantic to the Pacific Ocean. They finally took another ship up the coast to California. These gold hunters became known as "Forty-niners," because the year was 1849.

On the West Coast, legends and tales about gold were becoming "as thick as mosquitoes along the San Joaquin River." Some of them were true.

According to one story, a ten-year-old boy named Perkins was looking for a stone for his slingshot. He picked up a nugget worth a thousand dollars. This story is true.

But it was not true that a prospector found a mountain made of gold. Or that he died of excitement before he could hack it into nuggets. Such stories are "a dime a dozen."

Gold Rush Version of "Oh Susanna"

I come from Salem City,
With my washboard on my knee;
I'm going to California,
The gold dust for to see.

The pilot bread is in my mouth,
The gold dust in my eye,
And though I'm going far away,
Dear brothers, don't you cry.

I soon shall be in Francisco,
And then I'll look around,
And when I see the gold lumps there,
I'll pick them off the ground.

I'll scrape the mountains clean, my boys,
I'll drain the rivers dry,
A pocket full of rocks bring home,
So brothers, don't you cry!

Oh, California!
That's the land for me,
I'm going to Sacramento,
With my washboard on my knee.

Anonymous

THE BLUE BUCKET MINE

adapted from a story by Herman Oliver

Every mining country has its stories of lost mines. But of all stories, the one about the Blue Bucket Mine has been told the most—at least in Oregon where it supposedly happened.

The story starts at Fort Boise in Idaho. Six wagon trains pulled into that frontier post in August, 1845, and stopped for repairs.

"The Blue Mountain route is terrible, gentlemen, terrible," claimed Steve Meek. "But I know a cutoff route. It'll take you around the Blue Mountain, and save you 200 miles of hard travel."

So 200 wagons with about 1,000 people went with Meek. He charged $5.00 a wagon for his services.

The party left the Oregon Trail on August 24, 1845. That was the beginning of forty-five days of terror.

Meek's shortcut was "a sea" of boulders. The way was so rocky that many wagons shook to pieces. Horses and oxen laid down

boulders
(bōl' dərz)
large rocks

18

and refused to move. Their hoofs became so worn that each step left a bloody mark.

When the wagon train turned south to get out of the boulders, the party struck alkali water. It was undrinkable. And the travelers were in danger of dying of thirst.

"Where's Meek?" they asked. "We'll hang him!"

But Meek hid out. Later he returned with a rescue party and food.

Meanwhile the wagon train made camp. Everyone, even the children, began a search for water. Two boys and their sister, Mary, went north of the camp. There they found a place with many animal bones strewn around. That made them think that there once had been an old waterhole nearby. Maybe they could find a spring. So they began to dig.

Then Mary noticed some small golden pebbles in the dirt the boys were digging. The pebbles were so pretty that she stuck them in her pocket. When the boys finally struck water, they ran back to camp with the good news. Before they left the spring, they hung their small blue water bucket on a tree as a marker.

wagon train
group of wagons traveling overland

alkali water
(al' kə lī)
water with bitter, burning substances dissolved in it

In the meantime, other members of the train had already found a much larger spring. And the children's spring was forgotten.

A few years later, a member of the party discovered that the rocks Mary still carried were gold nuggets. In time, Mary's brothers decided to go back to Oregon to find their "Blue Bucket Mine." They found the general area. But they were unable to find the exact spot because of landslides.

Since then, many people have searched for the lost Blue Bucket Mine. But it has never been found.

LUCKY STRIKE

collected by
Henry Winfred
Splitter

Thousands of people caught the gold fever, and joined the rush to California in 1849. Few of them ever found gold and became rich. Many of them died on the trail. A few of them had all the luck. They were the ones that struck it rich. George Hearst was one of the lucky ones. Here's his story in his own words:

I was forty-nine years old when the discovery of silver in Nevada made the whole coast wild. I had been disappointed in the work I had been at. And I found myself pretty nearly broke. I had enough to buy a horse and outfit.

That broke me (took all my money) and I wasn't feeling happy. I started over the mountains with a party of the boys. There were about ten or twelve of us in the party. I was sad, so they left me alone.

My mustang was tired. So I stopped on the trail, put my arm through the bridle, and picked out a rock to sit on.

The rest of the boys rode on, but I sat there. There wasn't any reason why I should, particularly, only I did. As I sat there I thought, "Shall I go with them, or shall I go back?"

I thought and I thought. I saw behind me all the hard work I'd done, all the chances I'd

mustang
(mus′ tang)
small, wild horse
of the North
American plains

bridle
(brī′ dl)
part of a harness
that fits over a
horse's head

21

taken and lost on. I felt old and used up and no good. My sense told me to turn back and make my fight where I was known. There was safety in that, anyhow. But I'd been camping night after night with the boys ahead of me. It made me feel lonesome to think of parting company with them. I mounted my horse again and rode after the party. I'm glad I did.

Six months later I found gold and made a half million dollars. That was the foundation of what I've done since.

Now, why shouldn't I have turned back when I hesitated? It would have been sensible to do that. But I didn't. And because I didn't, I won. If you're ever inclined to think there's no such thing as luck, just think of me and keep looking.

"The best business you can go into you will find on your father's farm or in his workshop. If you have no family or friends to aid you, and no prospect opened to you there, turn your face to the great West, and there build up a home and fortune."

—Horace Greeley

Maria's Adventures in New Spain

collected by
Cheryl G. Hoople

Maria Antonia Pico was a member of one of California's first families. She lived in the world of New Spain on a ranch near Monterey, California. She often told her children and grandchildren this story of her escape from pirates:

It was about the middle of November, 1818, and I was sixteen. News came to us that a fleet of pirate ships was coming. Everyone was terrified. We began to move and hide our valuable things.

My father was not at home. But my mother and I packed many belongings in rawhide bags. We sent everything to the *cañada prieta*, or black ravine, twelve miles inland.

My brother, sister, and I went with the carts. Mother was to come the next day, with a servant, José. Night came on before we started, and it began to rain. As we went on, the rain grew worse. The oxen wanted to turn back. But we pushed on to carry out our mother's orders.

About midnight we reached a large, broken oak tree. Our mother had told us to camp

rawhide
(rô′ hīd′)
untanned, untreated skin of cattle

ravine
(rə vēn′)
long, deep, narrow valley eroded by running water

23

there. We let the oxen loose to graze. Then we crawled under the cart, wet to the skin.

Morning was dawning when we saw a large California lion, or puma. It was pulling the meat from one of our oxen. I whispered to the others to lie still, because we had no place to hide. As soon as it saw us, the puma walked up very close. He had a very curious, wondering look on his face. Then he went all around the cart, looking us over, and making a purring sound. We sat close and had our arms around one another. But we did not say a word.

The puma came up so close that I felt its breath on me. Finally, it put its nose against my ankle. I had no stockings on, only homemade shoes, and his nose felt very strange. I expected to be eaten up at once.

24

After what seemed a long time, the lion left us alone. He lay down by the dead ox, about 100 feet away. But he watched us most of the time.

About three o'clock in the afternoon, Mother and José came down from the coast way. From a high ridge they could look into the canyon and see everything. There we were, huddled under the cart, with the lion and dead ox nearby. José ran forward and fired two shots. He wounded the lion, but it got away in the rocks.

Later, Mother told me that she had forgotten a family book with writing of her father's in it. It was on a shelf in the house. She wanted to ride back to get it because she treasured it very much. I told her that I would go for her. I was not afraid to go.

So after we had our meal, I galloped off for Monterey. At last I reached the *lomita* (little hill) near the Plaza de Doña Brigida.

There were boats and men on the beach. Some of the houses were on fire. I turned a little and rode across the ridge. Then I went down a canyon to our own house. It was about a mile from the beach. I ran in and found the old book. I wrapped it in a piece of calfskin to tie behind the saddle. But when I

went out of the door, I saw my horse running off. It had been frightened away.

There was no other horse at the house—all had been turned loose. I ran over a little hill to the next ranch house. But all the people had gone. I was determined to catch a horse somehow.

But just then two men came out of the bushes. They spoke to me. They were armed and dangerous looking. So I fell on my knees and begged them to do me no harm. One of them asked me my name, and why I was there. So I told him and showed the book. He laughed and said I was a good girl. Then he sent his man to catch my horse. The man came up with my horse. I looked at the leader of the two and asked what he was going to do with me.

He looked at me and took a great oath. "My girl," he said, "you are braver than some of your people were on the beach. You shall go back." He put me up on my horse and kissed my hand. I rode off to our camp.

When I reached Mother's camp, I was crying. All that I could say was "Hasten, hasten!" We left all our things hidden in the bushes. We went on to the Salinas River. We met many families of fugitives. For nearly two weeks we lived in huts near the river. But in December the frightened people thought it was safe to move back to Monterey.

fugitives
(fyü′ jə tivz)
people who are
running away

TANGLING WITH A GRIZZLY

A. E. Schraff

**"Danger doesn't come with a bell
around its neck."**

—Finnish proverb from Oregon

*Some "unbelievable" stories are true. This old-
time story is an actual account of Allen B.
Light's encounter with a ferocious bear.*

A young man rode slowly through the canyon, his rifle at his side. He was a good
hunter, but he did not hunt for sport. He
hunted because he had to. And this afternoon
Allen had to find game or he and his friends
would go hungry.

"There's no more game in the mountains,"
his friend Jim had told him that morning.
"The snows will be here soon and we'll be
trapped for the winter without food. We'll
starve."

canyon
(kan'yən)
narrow valley
with high, steep
sides

game
(gām)
wild animals,
birds, or fish
hunted for sport
or for food

27

blizzard
(bliz′ ərd)
very cold,
blinding
snowstorm with
a very strong
wind

"There's still game in the mountains and I'm going to find it before the snow flies," Allen answered.

"Don't be a fool. If you go back into the mountains, you'll get caught in a blizzard. There's snow in those clouds," replied Jim.

Allen laughed, but deep in his heart he was worried.

He rode for most of the day without seeing even a rabbit. The wind was cold and the smell of snow was in the air. The gray clouds had turned black. And the sun was fading fast.

Then he saw a large deer—large enough to provide food for a long time.

Allen raised his rifle slowly. He had to get the deer with his first shot. If he shot, and missed, the deer might be frightened away.

He fired. His shot was true. He leaped off his horse and ran to where he had seen the deer fall. His heart raced with excitement. Tonight would be a time of celebration for everyone in the party. They would have food.

Suddenly, a huge bear leaped out of the brush and threw Allen to the ground. He cried out in pain as the bear clawed at him.

Allen was strong enough to win a fight with any man who ever lived. But the grizzly bear had terrific strength. Allen's coat was torn to pieces. One of his arms was almost torn off.

brush
(brush)
shrubs, bushes,
and small trees
growing thickly
in the woods

He became weaker and weaker from loss of blood. Yet the bear and the man wrestled wildly. They rolled over and over, first one on top, then the other. The furious battle lasted no more than three minutes.

Then, suddenly the bear stood up on its hind legs. Its huge body blotted out the last sunlight. Allen grabbed his gun. He had only one chance to hit the bear. If he missed, he would be dead in a moment.

He aimed his gun and fired. The bear crashed to the ground.

Slowly the man rose. He stared at the dead bear. He couldn't believe he had lived through a fight with this huge animal. The fight had been so furious that the brush all around had been crushed flat.

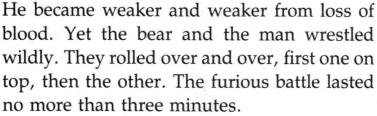

Allen strapped the deer to his saddle. He was hurt and tired, but he still had a job to do. There was no time to lose. The storm was upon him.

Darts of ice struck his face. The sun disappeared in the gloom and dark of rolling storm clouds. Within those clouds a blizzard was brewing.

He mounted his horse and headed out of the mountains. Allen was fighting against time now. He had to reach his camp before the storm broke. His life and the lives of the others depended on it.

. . .

Jim shouted, "Look! He's back! Allen's back and he has game!"

The injured man managed to smile. "I said I would come back with food, didn't I?"

But Jim only stared at him. "You're half dead!" he said.

Allen grinned. "Just so it's only half. I can't complain. The grizzly bear is worse off than I am."

"You fought a grizzly bear?" Jim asked.

"Yes. Had to. I'm all right, if you'll just take care of my arm. But remind me not to tangle with any more grizzly bears. They sure can tire a man out!"

Skills

Tangling with a Grizzly

Thinking About the Story

1. Allen Light's friends knew they might starve without new food supplies for the winter. Still Jim told Allen not to go back into the mountains. Why did he go hunting again in spite of Jim's warnings? Why didn't they ride to the nearest town for food?

2. Why did the bear attack Allen Light? Compare this story with Maria Antonia Pico's adventure with the puma. (See page 24.) Pioneers had to fight in the wilderness to survive. Discuss the hardships each character faced in order to survive.

3. Did Allen bring both the deer and the bear back to camp? Why or why not?

4. Allen B. Light's experience of being surprised by a wild animal was fairly common before 1900. Why?

Doing Things

1. Allen Light climbed mountains and crossed rivers few people had ever crossed before. What places would you like to explore that few people have ever seen?

2. Allen B. Light was a pioneer hero. Who are modern-day heroes? Are they fire fighters? astronauts? presidents? movie stars? Write a story about a modern-day hero.

Coming to America:
Miki Akiyama Uchida's Story

collected by Carol Ann Bales

Hundreds of thousands of Japanese began immigrating to America in 1868. Miki Akiyama Uchida was among the last of this great wave of immigrants. She was born in 1903 in Japan. She came to the United States with her husband, Tadatomo, in 1921. Here is her story in her own words:

greenhouse
(grēn'hous')
building with a
glass roof and
glass sides kept
warm for
growing plants

My husband, Tadatomo Uchida, was working in a greenhouse in the United States. He had returned to Japan to find a wife and asked about me. I was eighteen then. At first my mother refused. Finally she said OK. And that's how I came to this country.

I already knew something about America. When I was little, my older brother used to send me postcards from America. I thought that America was a beautiful place.

My future husband told my mother we would return in three years to visit. But my mother said, "If you come back in five or ten years, that's pretty good."

She was right. I didn't go back to see her. I had four children right away. And then my husband needed help in the greenhouse.

We came in a boat—no airplanes then. Fourteen days in a boat, and the first few days made you seasick. The boat was rocking and everything was sliding around. It took four or five days to calm down.

People already living in America gave me all kinds of advice. "When you go to America," they said, "go work in somebody's home, do housework. And you will learn English."

When we came to the port of Seattle, Washington, it was nighttime. And we could see the lights of the city all over the hills. It was so beautiful. But I was afraid to leave the boat. I didn't know what would happen.

A friend of my husband's drove us the five miles to our house. It was April when I came. All the cherry blossoms and pear trees and spring flowers were blooming. It was a beautiful setting.

We weren't far from the Pacific Ocean. In springtime it was warm and moist. Everyone had a beautiful lawn. In Japan you don't see that. I still get homesick for Seattle in the springtime. You could raise different kinds of flowers.

I came to this country during the busy season in the greenhouse. And I didn't have a chance to go to school to learn English. That's why my English is poor.

My husband told me to say the flower's name in English. I wrote down the name in Japanese. Next to it I wrote the English sound, and that way I remembered.

I learned to speak some English from a family that lived next door. They were people from Norway, very nice people. And I studied with my children when they went to school. I tried to talk only English with my children.

I learned English from the funny papers, too. I'd look at the pictures, and pretty soon I could understand what they were saying. And that's how I started to read.

Everything was fine for years. Then the greenhouse business wasn't like it was when I came. My first son went to Chicago and got a job. He said to come there and live with him.

We went to Chicago. I got a job as a dressmaker, and my husband went to work as a cabinetmaker. And we've stayed here ever since. When we could, my husband and I took out our citizenship papers.

(Although she and her family had many disappointments as aliens, she still says:)

I'm thankful to be living in the United States. The country is wonderful to us. All my children grew up here and have nice homes and families. I think America is a beautiful place.

aliens
(ā′lyənz)
foreigners

34

SOURDOUGH SALLY

Helen Louise Miller

Characters

SALLY CRANE,	*who wants to be a sour-dough*
MOTHER,	*Mrs. Crane*
DAISY	
EDITH	*Sally's friends*
THORA	*Sally's friends who are*
KOOTUK	*Eskimo twins*
SOURDOUGH CHARLIE,	*a classmate*
MISS COLLINS,	*a teacher*

Other classmates dressed as prospectors

Time: *The present. A spring day.*
Setting: *The Crane living room in Alaska.*
At Rise: SALLY CRANE *is sitting on a couch finishing a painting of the Alaska flag. The flag has eight gold stars on a blue field, arranged to represent the Big Dipper and the North Star. She holds it up to show to her mother.*

MOTHER. That's a fine flag, Sally. Every star is perfect, and the Dipper is just right.
SALLY. Do you think Miss Collins will use it for the school play?
MOTHER. I hope so, dear.

Big Dipper
group of seven bright stars that look like the handle and cup of a dipper (also called the Great Bear)

North Star
bright star almost directly over the North Pole

SALLY. It's such a beautiful flag and so right for Alaska, the land of the North Star.

MOTHER. I can hardly believe you are the same Sally who was so homesick when we first came. Now you're a regular little sourdough.

SALLY. But I'm not a *real* sourdough. The others say I'm still a *Chee-cha-ko,* a newcomer! Oh, Mother, I do hope I am chosen to say the poem about the flag. I know every word of it.

MOTHER. Maybe you will be chosen.

SALLY. But they are choosing the parts today, and I've been absent a whole week. I've missed all the fun and excitement of the spring breakup.

MOTHER. You even talk like a sourdough. A year ago you weren't the least bit interested in the ice breaking up.

SALLY. That's because I'd never lived through an Alaskan winter. Believe me, spring is something to celebrate up here. That's why we're having our play.

MOTHER. Well, I have a surprise for you. Since you are so much better, some of your friends will be stopping by after school today.

SALLY. That's great! Now I'll hear all the news. (*Doorbell*) I'll get it. (SALLY *puts the flag down carefully on a chair, then goes to the door.* MOTHER *exits.*)

CLASSMATES (*ad lib*). Hi, Sally! How do you feel?

SALLY. Oh, I feel fine now.

CLASSMATES. We've missed you.

THORA. *Everybody* missed you. The others are coming along. They stopped at the trading post. Mr. Smith has a grizzly bear down there. They wanted to see it.

trading post
frontier store

SALLY. Oh, I've seen that old stuffed grizzly lots of times.

KOOTUK. You haven't seen this one, Sally. It's alive!

EDITH. A real, live grizzly bear!

SALLY. What is he going to do with it?

KOOTUK. Return it to the woods, I guess. Right now he's taking care of it at the post. (*Doorbell*) I'll bet that's the rest of the gang now. Wait till you see them!

> (KOOTUK *admits six classmates dressed in jeans. They are wearing beards and carrying spades over their shoulders. The sixth one,* SOURDOUGH CHARLIE, *carries a pie pan. They march on stage to the tune of "Clementine." They form a semicircle around* SOURDOUGH CHARLIE.)

SOURDOUGH CHARLIE (*with a bow*). Howdy, Sally! Glad you're all well again!

ALL. (*They sing*).
In Alaska, in Alaska
In the land of ice and snow,

Lived a miner, ninety-niner,
Making bread with sourdough.

In the Yukon, in the Yukon,
Where the men all searched for gold,
Sourdough Charlie has made a fortune,
So the story has been told.

Sourdough Charlie, Sourdough Charlie,
Sourdough Charlie won us fame.
Though he's lost and gone forever,
True Alaskans bear his name.

SALLY (*wistfully*). That was wonderful. Are all the parts given out?

EDITH. Most of the speaking parts.

SALLY. Who is to say the poem about our state flag?

KOOTUK. Miss Collins hasn't decided yet.

SALLY. Thank goodness! Do you think I have a chance?

EDITH. You're a good speaker, Sally, but you're still a *Chee-cha-ko.*

SALLY. I am not! I am not a *Chee-cha-ko!* We've lived here almost a year.

THORA. But you're not a sourdough.

SALLY. That's not fair! This is my state just as much as yours, even if I wasn't born here.

SOURDOUGH CHARLIE. Did you ever throw a stone in the Yukon?

SALLY. Sure I did, lots of times.

KOOTUK. Well, did you ever pat a grizzly?

SALLY. What's that got to do with being a sourdough?

THORA. Everyone knows you have to throw a stone in the Yukon and pat a grizzly bear before you can become a sourdough. And I wouldn't advise patting a grizzly!

EDITH. Not if you want to stay all in one piece! A grizzly would tear you apart!

SALLY. But I want to be a sourdough more than anything else in the world.

DAISY. Forget it, Sally. Nobody pays any attention to that any more.

SALLY. But if I'm not a sourdough, I won't get to recite the poem about the flag.

THORA. There are plenty of other parts.

PROSPECTOR 1. Somebody has to tell about the history of Alaska.

PROSPECTOR 2. How it was purchased by Secretary Seward from Russia in 1867.

PROSPECTOR 3. And how everyone made fun of it and called Alaska "Seward's Folly" and "America's Icebox."

EDITH. Miss Collins just taught us a new poem about being voted the forty-ninth state.

PROSPECTOR 4. Maybe we should recite it right now and our speech of welcome, too.

SALLY. Why don't you go ahead and practice. I'll get some cookies.

Seward's Folly Seward's foolishness. In 1867 people did not think Alaska was worth $7 million. So they joked about the Secretary of State's purchase.

SOURDOUGH CHARLIE. Good! I never could work on an empty stomach. Come on, line up, everybody! *(They all line up behind* SOURDOUGH CHARLIE.*)*

ALL:

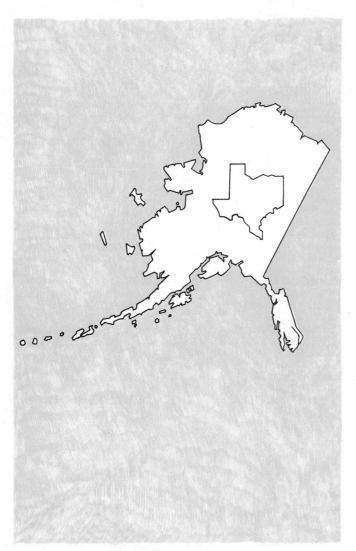

Howdy, Folks!
And welcome be ye
To the forty-ninth state
In the land of the free.

'Tis a great land, Alaska,
And double the size of
The big state of Texas,
The Westerner's prize.

Our winters are long,
And our summers are short,
But here we have fishing
And every great sport.

Our riches are many,
Our wealth is untold,
And people still come here
A-searching for gold.

Alaska, the Northland,
Of ice and of snow,
The land of the dogsled
And the Eskimo!
(Applause)

KOOTUK. And now for the statehood poem.
ALL. In nineteen hundred fifty-eight,
July the seventh was the date—

A new state joined your land and mine,
Alaska, number forty-nine!

(*During this poem* MOTHER *enters with* MISS COLLINS. *At the close of poem they both applaud.*)

MISS COLLINS. Bravo! Bravo! I hope you all do as well the day of the program.

ALL (*surprised*). Miss Collins! How did you get here?

MOTHER. I met her in town, and she says she has a special surprise for Sally. Where is Sally, by the way?

DAISY. She just went out to the kitchen to get some cookies.

MOTHER. That's fine. I'll go help her fix something cold to drink. (MOTHER *exits.*)

MISS COLLINS. I hope none of you told Sally our secret.

KOOTUK. Wild horses wouldn't get it out of us.

MISS COLLINS. That's good! I can hardly wait to see her face.

(MOTHER *reenters, upset.*)

MOTHER. Sally's not in the kitchen. What's happened to her?

SOURDOUGH CHARLIE. She said she was going for cookies.

MOTHER. But she's not there, and her coat is gone from the closet.

MISS COLLINS. Why would she leave the house when she has company?

THORA. Oh, no! You don't think—

MOTHER. Think what? Thora, do you know where Sally went?

THORA. Well, no, not exactly, but—we were all teasing Sally about being a *Chee-cha-ko*. We told her that old joke about what you have to do to be a sourdough.

MOTHER. Just what do you mean?

SOURDOUGH CHARLIE. Oh, it's all pretty silly, Mrs. Crane, and I didn't think Sally would take it seriously. There's an old saying that if you want to be a true sourdough, you have to throw a stone in the Yukon, and— and—

MOTHER. Well, go on.

SOURDOUGH CHARLIE. And pet a grizzly.

MOTHER. Pet a grizzly! Thank goodness there are no grizzlies around here, or she just might be foolish enough to try.

SOURDOUGH CHARLIE. That's the trouble, Mrs. Crane. We were telling her about the big grizzly down at the trading post. We never thought she'd fall for it.

MOTHER. But where is she then?

MISS COLLINS. Now don't be upset, Mrs. Crane. Sally is too sensible to do anything so dangerous.

MOTHER. But you don't know how badly she wants to be a sourdough. I'm going down there right away. If she tries to pat that grizzly, she's sure to get badly hurt.

(MOTHER *goes to get her coat. Just then,* SALLY *enters, beaming with joy. She is wearing a coat and carries a letter in an envelope.*)

ALL. Sally! Sally!

MOTHER. Sally Crane, where have you been? You've scared the life out of us!

SALLY. I don't see why. I wore my coat, and the trading post isn't very far.

SOURDOUGH CHARLIE. Don't tell me you tried to pat that grizzly!

SALLY. I not only tried, I did it! Oh, hello, Miss Collins. I'm so glad you're here. You can read my letter from Mr. Smith to prove I patted a grizzly.

MISS COLLINS *(reads)*. "This is to certify that Sally Crane patted a real, full-grown grizzly bear at the trading post on this last day of April, 1980. Signed, Preston R. Smith, Proprietor."

MOTHER. Sally! That bear could have hurt you seriously.

SALLY. Oh, no, it couldn't! It was dead!

ALL. Dead!

SALLY. Nothing in the rules said the grizzly had to be alive. I just patted that old stuffed one Mr. Smith has had for twenty years.

DAISY *(laughing)*. You really played a trick on us!

SALLY. And now you can't call me a *Chee-cha-ko* anymore. I'm a real sourdough like the rest of you.

MISS COLLINS. What you don't know, Sally, is that you have been an honest-to-goodness sourdough for the past week.

44

SALLY. How?

MISS COLLINS. The real test of a sourdough is living through an Alaskan winter from one spring ice break to another. When that ice began to melt last week, you and your whole family became official sourdoughs.

SALLY. But why didn't somebody tell me?

CHILDREN. It was a secret.

MISS COLLINS. And everyone voted that you should have the honor of making the closing speech about our flag.

SALLY. Thank you! I can't believe it! Thank you!

MOTHER (*taking* SALLY's *flag off the chair*). That's wonderful, Sally! And look at this. Here's a flag Sally made for the school play.

MISS COLLINS. It's lovely and just the size we need for the program. Now I think it's high time for us to have a rehearsal. Sourdough Charlie, make your speech.

SOURDOUGH CHARLIE (*stepping forward with a bow*). Ladies and gentlemen, as the final number of our spring program, we will have a tribute to the Alaskan state flag by our own Sourdough Sally!

SALLY (*taking the flag*). This beautiful flag that we all love and respect was designed by a thirteen-year-old Indian boy named Benny Benson. When Benny designed our flag, he was a seventh-grade pupil at the Mission

School in Seward. His design was officially adopted by our legislature in 1927. Today our Alaskan flag takes its place with the flags of the other states that make up our great union. So wherever this flag flies, Alaskans are reminded of their love of country and their pride in the last frontier.

Alaska's flag is filled with stars.
The Dipper points the way
To where the North Star holds its place,
A steady, shining ray.
The North Star is a friendly guide
To sailors lost at sea,
To trappers lost in fields of snow,
And even you and me.
Alaska's flag, a beacon light,
A flag we all hold dear,
Its eight gold stars on field of blue,
Salute the last frontier.

(All sing "God Bless America" as curtains close.)

Sourdough Sally

Thinking About the Story

1. This is a story about Alaska. It is also a story about a stranger getting used to a new land, just as the pioneers did. If you were suddenly to move to Alaska, in what ways would it be difficult? pleasant? Is there such a thing as a modern pioneer? Why or why not?

2. What is a "spring breakup"? Why do people in Alaska celebrate the spring breakup?

3. A true Alaskan is called a sourdough. What is a newcomer called? How can a newcomer become a "true Alaskan"? How does a newcomer in your home state become a "true home-stater"?

4. Using facts and information from the play, make a report on the state of Alaska.

Doing Things

1. Paint or draw a picture of Alaska's flag or your own state flag. Display it in the classroom. Find out about the history of your state flag. Write a speech about it and recite the speech.

2. *Sourdough Sally* is a play. It is meant to be performed. This can be an exciting class project.

History on a Map

A map is like a history book. A name on a map can tell a lot more than you might think at first.

Look at a map of the Pacific States, for example. Pioneers came into the territory from all over the world. They brought along their Old World names.

You will find Swisshome and Norway in Oregon. Manchester, Melbourne, and Normandy Park are places in Washington. But you can also find those names in England, Australia, and France.

As for California, almost every other name is Spanish. In the San Francisco Bay Area alone are San Rafael, San Mateo, San Pablo, El Cerrito, Palo Alto, and Vallejo. Those are just a few. Venice, Dublin, Muscoy, and Delhi are California cities, too. Those names come from Italy, Ireland, Russia, and India. And China Lake and Half Moon Bay remind us of our Chinese forefathers.

Many Alaskan towns have Eskimo names. There are Akolmiut and Kasiglut and Kiualina. But Alaska is also the home of Dutch Harbor and English Bay. A cape in Alaska is still called "Glory of Russia."

What brought all these settlers to the Pacific States? Freedom! Adventure! Gold! Fur! Land!

California has a city named Freedom, and one called Independence. There is also Independence, Oregon. If you are looking for Freeland and Liberty, head for Washington.

Gold was discovered in California in 1848. That brought on the great gold rush of 1849. California's nickname is the "Golden State" and "El Dorado State." Two cities in California are golden. There are *Oro Grande* and *Oroville. Oro* is the Spanish word for gold.

If you are looking for Gold Beach and Gold Hill, visit Oregon. Gold Bar and Goldendale are Washington cities. And Alaska has a town called Platinum!

There is a funny story about North Bloomfield, California. It used to be named Humbug back in the old gold rush days. A man came into town and started to brag about striking it rich.

"Why, there's gold there, lying right on the ground!" he said. "When the wind blows a bit, gold dust blows down your throat. Every time you sneeze you lose some money."

A lot of gold rushers left to work the stream but they found no gold. So they named the place Humbug.

Many cities' names reflect the rich animal life found in the Pacific States. Settlers and hunters counted on animals for food and furs. This explains why places were named Otter Island, Fox Islands, Kodiak, Bear Mountain, Beaver Creek, and Moose Pass. These are towns in Alaska. California is the home of Big Bear City and Seal Beach. Antelope, Beaver, Grizzly, Fox, Elk Lake, and Otter Rock are all Oregon cities. Washington also has its share of cities named for animals. Take Badger Mountain, Elk, Deer Park, and Fox Islands.

Hawaii is something of an exception in matters of names. Most Hawaiian city names are Polynesian. Hawaii was originally Havaiki. It was named after a lost ancient homeland. All the islands have names given by their first inhabitants. Oahu means "the gathering place." Kauai is "the garden isle." And Mt. Haleakala means "the house of the sun."

How did your city get its name? How did other towns around your area get their names? You read a lot of history when you read a map.

---

platinum (plat′nəm) heavy, silver-white precious metal

inhabitants (in hab′ə tənts) people or animals that live in a place

FOLLOWING OLD FOOTPRINTS

Footprints

There is joy in
Feeling the warmth
Come to the great world
And seeing the sun
Follow its old footprints
In the summer night.

There is fear in
Feeling the cold
Come to the great world
And seeing the moon
—Now new moon, now full moon—
Follow its old footprints
In the winter night.

collected by Knud Rasmussen;
an Eskimo chant

THE LOON'S NECKLACE

collected by Allan A. MacFarlan

This story of the loon and the blind man is found throughout the Pacific Northwest and all over North America. Over fifty-six versions have been collected. It has traveled by word of mouth into many different Indian and Eskimo languages. This version tells how the loon, a water bird, got its beautiful neckband of white feathers.

medicine man
(med′ə sən)
man supposed to
have magic
power

Dark Night, the medicine man, sat facing the warm afternoon sun. He felt the warmth of autumn on his face. He heard the rustle of the woodland animals. But his eyes did not see the great eagle drifting overhead. Dark Night was blind.

"Why not weave baskets or make arrows like other men who live in the night shadows?" asked his wife. "If you did, we could trade them for food and skins. We would not be hungry and cold when winter comes."

Dark Night listened but he did not answer.

totem
(tō′ təm)
natural object
taken as the sign
of a tribe, clan,
or family

"Call on your secret totem to help us now," begged his wife.

52

"When the time comes, I will," he promised.

Autumn passed. Winter came on a wild north wind.

The fear of hunger was in the hearts of the people. Even before the snow, hunting had been bad. Now it was worse. Bands of hunters returned to the village empty-handed. There were neither animals nor birds to be found. The best hunters in the tribe spent long cold days on the trail. But they brought back no food.

The chief of the tribe sent out the young warriors. They went through the deep snow to neighboring tribes. They carried beads and weapons to trade for food. They returned with the same beads and weapons they had taken. Their neighbors, too, hungered for food. They had none to spare.

On a bitter cold night, Dark Night lay awake in his lodge. He heard the loon's warning cry overhead. It rang out four times. Instantly, Dark Night fell asleep and dreamt. In his dream he saw sorrow, danger, and death. He heard the hungry cry of wolves coming nearer and nearer. The cry of the loon awoke him. He thought about the wolves' cries and the loon's warning as daybreak came.

Dark Night left the lodge early and made

lodge
(loj)
place to live in; house

53

his way to the council lodge. There the chief sat with the wise men of the tribe. Dark Night stood before them. He told them of his dream. "This is how it will be. Starving wolf packs will attack the village in four days."

"I would laugh," said the tribal medicine man, "but I am too hungry."

The wise men smiled, but were silent.

When the people of the village heard Dark Night's warning, they made fun of him. They no longer believed in his medicine. They pointed their mocking fingers at him and tried to forget their hunger.

On the fourth day, as night fell, the savage wolf packs came. They raided the village, killing many men, women, and children. Each night the wolves attacked and killed. For days, the brave warriors feared to leave the village.

Finally, the chief asked Dark Night to come to the council lodge. Dark Night made his way through the deep snow to the meeting place. He was guided to the place of honor beside the chief. This time the chief and his wise men did not make fun of him. "It has been said you have a bow," said the chief. "It is said that the arrows shot from this bow cannot miss. Let our best hunter use it against the wolves that will come tonight."

"No one but I can bend the magic bow," declared Dark Night. "Tonight I will use it. Have the young warriors bring me many arrows."

"You will have all of the best arrows," promised the chief.

That night when the wolves attacked again, Dark Night dressed in his best buckskin hunting dress. With a great warrior leading him, he circled the village. When he heard the movement of a wolf, he placed an arrow in the bow. He pointed the magic bow in the direction of the wolf. The arrow sang through the night.

When dawn came, many gray bodies were stretched out on the snow. All of the wolves had been killed.

Soon spring arrived and the snows vanished. Deer returned to the forest and the people were happy once more.

Dark Night sat outside his lodge. From the lake came the clear cry of a loon. Four times the loon called.

Dark Night dressed himself in his finest buckskin once again. Around his neck he placed a beautiful necklace of gleaming, snow-white shells. Taking his walking stick, he made his way through the forest, following the loon call to the lake. When the loon cry seemed directly in front of him, Dark Night stopped. His hand held the trunk of a tree. Through his moccasins he could feel sand at the edge of the lake.

Suddenly, the loon call broke the silence. Never before had Dark Night heard the notes so loud and clear. He trembled. Then he spoke, "Oh Father Loon, my totem bird, I have a wish I beg you to grant."

"Speak, my son, so that I may know your wish," replied the loon.

"For many moons I have lived in the deepest, darkest night. I can only imagine the wonders of this world. I beg you, let my eyes see."

"Faith made you believe. Faith will make you see," replied the loon. "Climb onto my back. Hold tight to my wings."

Dark Night was afraid, but he did as he was told. He took the loon's wings in his hands. The great bird dove into the lake. Dark Night felt the cold waters flow against his face.

When they reached the other side, the loon spoke. "Has the light come to your eyes, my son?"

"No, Father Loon, all is still dark."

Again the loon dove smoothly into the water. It swam to the opposite shore. Then

moons
(münz)
lunar months;
each about 29½
days

the loon asked again, "Has light come to your eyes, my son?"

"Not yet, Father Loon. I see only a grayness before me."

When the lake had been crossed a third time, the loon asked again. "Has the light come?"

"Yes, Father Loon. I can see now, but dimly."

The loon warned Dark Night to hold on. Then it dove. Again the water flowed against the medicine man's eyes.

When they reached the shore, Dark Night flung his arms upward. "Father Loon," he cried, "I can see! How can I thank you? How can I ever repay you?"

His fingers quickly untied his greatest treasure—his shell necklace. His hands trembled as he dropped the glistening white shells over the loon's head.

The snowy collar of shells glittered against the loon's black feathers.

The great bird raised its head toward the sky. Four times its laugh filled the night with music.

The heart of the medicine man was glad. The shells had become a glistening feather necklace that the loon would wear forever.

57

The Loon's Necklace

Thinking About the Story

1. Why didn't Dark Night want to call on his secret totem in the beginning of the story? How did Dark Night's wife feel about this?

2. Reread pages 53–55. Why did the wolves attack Dark Night's village? Do you think the wolves had ever attacked the village before? Why?

3. How did the chief and the council treat Dark Night when he first warned them about the wolves? How did they treat him later? Why?

4. Reread paragraph 3 on page 55. What does the author mean by, "the arrow sang through the night"? What did Dark Night mean when he said, "For many moons I have lived in the darkest, deepest night"?

Doing Things

1. This legend tells how the loon got its white neckband. Write your own legend that explains how another animal got its special looks.

2. The loon's cries were a warning in the beginning of the story. At the end, the loon's laughter filled the night with music. Write a short song or poem about the loon's cries or laughter.

THE GODDESS OF THE VOLCANO

On the Big Island of Hawaii, there are many kinds of ghost stories. The Chinese and Koreans, as well as Hawaiians, told them. So did Puerto Ricans, Portuguese, and Okinawans. But the stories heard most often from all kinds of people in Hawaii are those of Pele, goddess of volcanoes.

Sometimes there are stories of Pele appearing as a beautiful young woman in a red muumuu. In others she appears as an old woman dressed in a black holoku. She is seen walking along a road with her small white dog.

"My grandfather saw her once, a long time ago," said a Chinese girl living in Hawaii. "He was driving his pickup truck. And there she was walking along the road. She was wearing a black holoku. And a little white dog trotted beside her.

"My grandfather stopped and offered her a ride. She got in and they drove for a mile or so. While my grandfather turned away to watch the road, she vanished. The woman and the dog were gone!

"There was no way they could have gotten out of the truck. But they were gone!

muumuu
(mü′mü′)
loose, bright,
often long dress,
originally worn
by Hawaiians

holoku
(hō′lō kü)
a very old-
fashioned style
of muumuu

59

eruption
(i rup′ shən)
bursting or
throwing forth

superstition
(sü′pər stish′ ən)
belief founded
on unreasoning
fear or trust in
magic

crater
(krā′ tər)
bowl-shaped
opening of a
volcano

"My grandfather said it was Madame Pele, the famous Goddess of the Volcano. She had come to warn the people that there would be a volcanic eruption.

"And do you know what? Two days later there was an eruption. Kilauea Crater erupted on the Big Island of Hawaii."

There are many stories about Madame Pele. All of them agree that she sought out the volcanoes because she was cold. She would dig day and night, into the heart of the volcano. When at last she reached its fiery heart she was happy. She wanted its warmth.

But whenever the volcano began to erupt, Madame Pele came down the mountain to roam. She came to warn the people.

Could this be true? Or is it just a ghost story? A superstition?

Whenever anyone has seen Madame Pele and her little white dog, a volcanic eruption has followed. . . . The fiery fountains soar hundreds of feet high. The noise is like thick oatmeal boiling on a giant stove. Once, in 1959, Kilauea's lava fountain soared 1900 feet high.

Many people who live near the volcanoes of Hawaii believe all this is true. They sometimes throw red lehua blossoms and ohelo berries in the craters. They hope to keep Madame Pele happy. This may not be scientific, but whenever the lady appears, they pay attention.

THE MYSTERY OF BIGFOOT

Daniel Cohen

Many sightings of a big, hairy, man-like creature have been reported in the Pacific Northwest.

People have seen its footprints. Photographs of the footprints have appeared in newspapers. Plaster casts of them were sized at fifteen to twenty-four inches long and six to twelve inches wide. The size of its tracks gives the creature its name—"Bigfoot." Indian tribes called a similar creature "Sasquatch." Sasquatch means "the one who runs and hides."

Bigfoot is said to be from six to nine feet tall. It has been seen walking on two legs. Reports have shown that it weighs over 300 pounds. And its body is completely covered with short, dark hair. Those who have seen its face say that Bigfoot looks like an ape. But they say it is strangely human.

plaster casts
(plas′ tər kasts)
molds or forms
made of plaster

On October 20, 1967, two "monster hunters" made an important sighting. Roger Patterson had been looking for the monster for
years. He had even written a book about Bigfoot. This time he was with his friend, Bob
Gimlin. They were traveling on horseback
near Bluff Creek, California. There had been
many earlier reports about Bigfoot from this
rugged country.

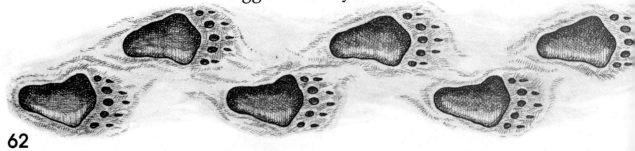

At 3:30 in the afternoon, they saw Bigfoot! It was just like the reports had said.

Patterson jumped from his horse and started taking motion pictures. Bigfoot took long strides and swung its arms. Patterson and Gimlin guessed that the creature was about eight feet tall. They said that it must have weighed several hundred pounds.

Their film was shown in some movie theaters. It gave audiences a glimpse of a furry figure. Some scientists thought the creature looked like a person in a monkey suit. There was no way to prove the film was real. But there was no way to prove it was a fake, either.

One man has claimed to have lived with a family of Bigfoots. Most of the reports of Bigfoot come from northern California, Washington, and Oregon.

. . .

Does Bigfoot exist? Are the large number of sightings and footprints enough to convince you? Compare the different footprints on these pages. Which do you think belong to Bigfoot? a human? a grizzly bear?

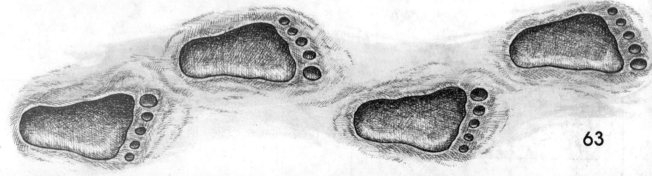

Pacific States Yesterday and Today

Things To Do: Write a story about a pioneer who enters a time machine and ends up in your state in the 1980s.

European and Chinese laborers at work on the Pacific Railroad.

Pony Express, fast mail service of the mid-1800s, saluting the telegraph.

A Nez Percé chief in front of a tepee.

Eskimo woman
weaving a basket.

Mission San Diego de Alcala,
California.

Hawaiian fisherman
throwing his net.

Space Needle, Seattle, Washington.

Rosebowl Parade, Pasadena, California.

Palomar Observatory, California.

66

Downtown
Anchorage, Alaska.

Downtown Portland, Oregon.

Watts Tower, Los Angeles,
California. Built by Simon
Rodia with old wire, pipe,
broken dishes, bed springs,
bottles, and seashells.

Lewis and Clark and Sacajawea

One of the world's most famous frontier guides was a woman. She spoke English, French, and Shoshoni and was good at Indian sign language. Her name was Sac-a-ja-we-a.

Mother Earth was Sacajawea's friend. Like the chipmunks, this Indian woman knew how to find food when it was scarce. Like the chickadees, she found hiding places in times of danger. Like the frogs and water birds, she knew the wonders and the dangers of shaded pools and open waterways. Like elk and deer, she could find the trailways through high and rugged mountains.

She traveled with Lewis and Clark on their exploring trip through the Northwest Territory: from a village of the friendly Mandan Indians in what is now North Dakota and into Montana, from Montana into what is now Oregon and Washington, and to the Pacific.

Even the birth of her child, a baby boy, did not trouble Sacajawea. She put the newborn child on a cradleboard and strapped it to her back. Then she continued the journey as strong and willing as ever.

Lewis and Clark said that Sacajawea was responsible for the success of their trip. "The Indian tribes knew that we came in peace when they saw an Indian woman in our party. Therefore they did not harm us."

There was great joy in their camp on November 8, 1804, when they sighted the great Pacific Ocean. The explorers danced along on the beach. They skipped in a circle and sang, over and over, "We're here! We're here!" They had traveled about 4,100 miles.

The trip had begun on April 7, 1804. On September 20, 1805—17 months later—the exploring party arrived back in St. Louis.

THE GHOSTLY HITCHHIKER

Ken Williams

Throughout the United States, stories are told about ghost riders. These tales vary from state to state. Here is one from California:

It was a dark, cold night. A man and woman were driving back into San Francisco from a Sunday outing. It had started to rain shortly before dark. Now the rain was beating hard against the windshield, making it hard for them to see the road.

As they came around a curve in the road, the headlights of their car suddenly shone on a hitchhiker. It was a young girl, wet to the skin. She was standing alone at the side of the highway. She waved her hand for a ride.

"John, look! There's a girl wanting a ride," said Edna in surprise. "What is she doing out on a night like this?"

"Shall we pick her up?" asked John, slowing the car down.

"Of course," said Edna. "Look at her . . . so wet and cold . . . oh, the poor thing."

The car stopped, and the girl ran toward the car with a look of thanks on her face. She wore a white dress—a party dress. But the rain had changed it into a dripping wet sack. It clung to her body. Her hair also hung in long wet strands. In her hand she carried a small bunch of roses, also wet and dripping.

"Want a ride?" John shouted above the roar of the wind and the rain.

"Yes, please," said the girl.

"We're going to San Francisco," said Edna. "You poor child, you're soaked to the skin.

Here, get in. And wrap yourself in this blanket. You must be very cold.''

"Thanks," said the girl. She crawled into
the back seat of the car and wrapped herself in
the blanket. "I hope I won't get the car seat
wet."

"Don't worry about that," said John.
"Where are you going?"

"To San Francisco," she answered.

"Well, you're in luck. That's where we're
going."

"Do you live there?" Edna asked.

71

"Yes."

"Where in the city do you live?"

There was a long silence before the girl answered, "I live at 1010 Sutter Street."

"That's not far out of our way, is it, John?" Edna asked.

"No. We go right by there," John answered. "We'll let you off at your front door."

The girl didn't answer. Presently, Edna looked back at her and then said softly to John, "She's asleep. She must have been at the end of her strength, the poor dear. I'm so glad we came along to help her."

John and Edna rode along in silence. Each was thinking about the girl and wondering what she was doing out on a night like this . . . in a party dress . . . with a bouquet of roses . . . all alone . . . far from the city. When at last they entered the city, they still rode in silence, not wanting to waken the girl.

At Dumbarton Bridge, John slowed down and stopped beside the guard at the toll booth. He rolled down his window and handed the guard seventy-five cents.

"For three of us," he said.

"Three?" said the guard. "You mean two."

"No, three," John answered. "Me and my wife and the girl in the back seat."

72

"What girl?" asked the guard, peering into the back seat. "There's no girl back there!"

John and Edna spun around and looked. The back seat was empty. Only the wet blanket remained.

"But—but she was there! We picked her up on the road! She sat right there, wrapped up in that blanket!"

"Look, mister," said the guard, "you can figure that out yourself. All I need is fifty cents for the *two* of you. We don't charge for ghosts. They can pass free."

"What should we do, Edna?" John asked. "Should we go back looking for the poor girl?"

"No, we probably wouldn't find her if we did." Edna thought a moment before she added, "Let's go to her house and inquire. If no one's home, then we'll go to the police."

They left the bridge and drove through the city. Both were disbelieving all of the thoughts spinning around their heads.

The car pulled up at 1010 Sutter Street. The porch light was on.

"Well, here we are," said Edna. "Oh, I do hope she's home . . . but how could she get here from the back seat of our car?"

"Well, we'd better find out," John said, stepping out of the car. "I hope she's home, too."

They walked up the steps and rang the doorbell. Presently the door opened.

Standing in the doorway was a middle-aged woman. "Yes?" she said.

John introduced himself and his wife. Then he began telling about the girl in the white dress. The woman listened to the entire story without saying a word.

"The girl said she lived at this address," Edna said. "Do you know anything about her?"

"Yes," said the woman quietly. "The girl is my daughter. She was killed in a car accident . . . ten years ago tonight . . . on the highway where you picked her up. Every year on this day, I have had a caller who tells the same story you just told."

As the woman slowly closed the door she added, "Thank you for being kind to her."

John and Edna walked back to the car.

"I really can't believe that, John," said Edna. "We're all dreaming! There really wasn't any girl. We're all just imagining this."

"You're probably right," John said.

Then he walked to the driver's side and opened the door. It was then that he saw the bouquet of roses . . . still wet with rain. The girl had dropped them . . . before she disappeared.

The Goddess of the Volcano /
The Ghostly Hitchhiker

Thinking About the Story

1. Why is Madame Pele called the Goddess of the Volcano? When do people see her? How do they recognize her?
2. What question might you ask yourself after reading "The Ghostly Hitchhiker"?
3. How are the Ghostly Hitchhiker and the Goddess of the Volcano alike? different? Can you find any evidence in the stories that they tried to frighten people?
4. Does Madame Pele really exist? What proof is given in the story? What proof did Edna and her husband have that the Ghostly Hitchhiker existed?

Doing Things

1. Earthquake! Geyser! Hot springs! Tornado! Hurricane! Make up a legend or ghost story to explain one of these natural happenings.
2. What did Madame Pele and the Ghostly Hitchhiker look like? Draw or paint a picture of them. The stories will give you clues about how each was dressed.

The Coming of the Salmon

collected by
Allan A. MacFarlan

The storyteller of the Haida Indian tribe faced the great Nhe-is-bik totem pole. There were children all around him as he began this story:

The little daughter of our chief was very, very unhappy. The girl was sad because no one could give her the great, shining fish she wanted. Her father was a powerful chief, but he had never seen such a fish. Even the wisest men of the tribe did not know where to find this fish.

The little girl grew unhappier with each passing day. So the chief ordered a great Council Fire.

All of the tribal medicine men sat around the fire. And the wisest of them rose to speak. "The maiden longs for a thing she has seen in a dream," he said. "We have many fish in our inlet, but none are like the one she describes. Such a fish may prove to be big medicine for our tribe if we can find it. Let our wise men speak. Maybe one of them knows where such a great, gleaming, leaping fish may be found."

Then the old medicine man stood and spoke. "Wise Raven, who lives among the cedar trees, is my good friend. He knows many things that the wisest among us do not know. Let me bring him to this Council Fire."

The chief liked the idea. And the old medicine man soon returned with Raven.

The great bird croaked as he spoke, and only the wisest men could follow his talk-trail. "What the daughter of the chief asks for is giant fish, known as Salmon," said Raven. "In this moon, they are to be found far from here, at the mouth of a mighty river. Because you are my friends, I will fly swift and far to bring one of these fish to your village."

Before the chief could thank Raven, the big bird was high in the air. It flew as far and fast as a harpoon travels. Then its keen eyes saw many Salmon swimming together at the mouth of the river. Raven dived quick as a hawk and, by chance, caught the little son of the Salmon Chief in his claws. With the fish held tightly in his claws, Raven flew toward the distant village of his friends.

A horde of Salmon, led by their chief, swam rapidly after Raven. Still the fast-flying bird reached the village far ahead of the Salmon.

inlet
(in'let)
narrow strip of
water running
into the land

gills
(gilz)
part of the body
of a fish by
which it breathes
in water

Raven placed the great fish before the little daughter of the chief. She smiled and pined no more. Then Raven told the old medicine man that many Salmon would soon swim to the inlet.

The medicine man told the chief what Raven had said. The chief told the fishermen and women to weave a huge net. This they did swiftly. And when the Salmon came, all of the fish were caught in the net.

To hold them, a long, strong strip of leather was passed through their gills. One end of this leather strip was tied to a big rock. The other end was fastened to a great totem pole, as tall as a cedar tree. Ever since, this totem pole has been called the Nhe-is-bik, or tethering pole.

As he spoke, the storyteller pointed to the totem pole. And the children saw the figures of a mighty thunderbird, an Indian chief, a raven, and salmon, in that order. They had been carved from the top of the great cedar pole to remind the Haida Indian tribe of the story of the Salmon.

"The end of my story tells of great magic," declared the storyteller. "Year after year, from that time to this, the salmon pass on this side of the inlet, and our people are glad."

THE MANSION OF THE DEAD

Jean Anderson

Just outside of San Francisco stands a five-million-dollar mansion. It is dark and empty. It is the Winchester House. Its strange story began about a hundred years ago in New Haven, Connecticut. Sarah Winchester is the main character. She was married to the heir of "the Winchester Rifle King." The Winchester Rifle was one of the best ever made. Hunters, soldiers, Indians, cowboys, bandits, and travelers used it. It was used for both killing and protection from being killed.

heir
(er *or* ar)
person who gets someone's property or title after that one dies

The story goes that Sarah had "second sight." That is, she spoke with the dead. No one knows if she was born with this "second sight" or if she developed it after tragedy struck.

Her tragedy was a swift double blow. Within a few months she lost her husband and her only child. And, to her friends, it seemed she lost her mind as well.

Sarah withdrew from the world. None of her doctors could cure her. So she began inviting mediums into her home. A "medium" is a person who supposedly can talk with the dead. Time and again mediums came. None of them could help her speak with her dead husband.

Finally, she heard about Adam Coons. He was a well-known medium. He gave her a message that would change her life.

"You must care for the ghosts who have been killed by Winchester rifles," Adam Coons said. "Or they will haunt you forever."

Sarah listened to everything Adam Coons told her. And she believed him. She moved to California. That is where Adam Coons had said her dead husband wanted her to buy a house. She was to rebuild this house. For she must "make room in it for all the ghosts."

For weeks, Sarah searched for the house without success. Finally, she visited an eight-room house in Santa Clara Valley. "This is it," a voice told her. And she knew her husband William had at last spoken to her.

Sarah set about her strange task of rebuilding and enlarging the house which sat on forty-four acres. She must make space for hundreds of ghosts killed by Winchester rifles.

She hired eighteen servants and an "army

of workers." Money was no problem. Sarah had a fortune worth twenty million dollars.

For thirty-six years, Sarah's workmen followed her commands. Year after year, seven days a week, they worked. When they finally completed the house, it sprawled over six acres of ground.

Rooms were tacked onto rooms. Stairways aimed into thin air. Doors opened onto blank walls. Secret passageways went nowhere. The sound of hammers and saws never stopped. There were in the end 160 rooms, 2,000 doors, 40 staircases, and 47 fireplaces.

Sarah also made sure that each chandelier had 13 lights. Each room had 13 windows. And each stairway had 13 steps. She believed that 13 is a lucky number. At dinner parties there were always 13 settings at her table. Master chefs prepared the meals for 12 ghostly guests and Sarah, 13 in all. Sarah always said she could see the 12 ghosts seated at the table.

chandelier (shan'də lir') fixture with branches for lights, usually hanging from the ceiling

In September of 1922, at the age of eighty-five, Sarah died. She left Winchester House to the ghosts.

Sarah's wishes are still honored. By day, the house is a tourist attraction. Guides warn visitors to stay close.

Most of the rooms, now, are sealed. They belong to Sarah and to the night. . . .

Extra! Extra!
Read All About It!

Earthquake Blasts
Los Angeles, Calif. April 8, 1906. An earthquake and fire struck San Francisco and neighboring towns today. Four square miles were on fire. Damage has been estimated at $350 million. More than 500 people are reported dead or missing.

Officials say the whole city will have to be rebuilt.

Volcano Blows its Top
Vancouver, Washington. May 19, 1980. The volcano Mount St. Helens blew its top yesterday. Mount St. Helens is in southwestern Washington. The explosion started some forest fires and spewed tons of ash. The sun was blotted out for hundreds of miles, turning day into night.

"The top of the mountain is no longer there," said a pilot who flew over Mount St. Helens today.

This is the most violent eruption of Mount St. Helens in 123 years.

Quake Shakes Alaska
March 27, 1964. Juneau, Alaska. An earthquake shook the area around Anchorage and Valdez today. High waves destroyed much property along the coast. At least 130 people were killed. Total damage was about $750 million.

Drive-in Volcanoes

There are a lot of active volcanoes in the Pacific Ocean states. Not all of them are dangerous. Katamai National Monument in Alaska is an area of active volcanoes and crater lakes. It includes a place called the Valley of Ten Thousand Smokes. Hot gases seep from cracks in the earth there.

On the island of Hawaii there are many volcanoes, including Mauna Loa and Kilauea. They are among the most active in the world. Their eruptions, however, do little damage, because the volcanoes do not explode. At Kilauea, streams of hot lava boil up to the top of the volcano and down the mountainside. They look like streams of fire. Tourists in cars and buses enjoy watching the bubbling lava and fire fountains. They call it a "drive-in volcano."

The Gift

'Tis the gift to be simple,
'Tis the gift to be free,
'Tis the gift to come down
Where you ought to be.

Joseph Brackett

TIMBER

LUMBERJACK'S ALPHABET

collected by Elmore Vincent
arranged by Nick Manoloff

A is the ax that cutteth the pine.
B is the jolly boys never behind.
C is the chopping when we begin.
D is the danger we oft are in.
E is the echo; hear the woods ring.
F is the foreman who laughs when we sing.
G is the grindstone; grind your ax good.
H is the handle of hickory wood.
I is the iron that marketh the pine.
J is the jolly boys feeling fine.
K is the keen-edge ax that we keep.
L is the lice that keep us from sleep.
M is the moss to chink up our camps.
N is the needle that sews up our pants.
O is the owl that hoots in the night.
P is the pine that we felled just right.
Q is the quarrels we have when in town.
R is the rivers we float the logs down.
S is the sleighs so stout and so strong.
T is the teams that haul them along.
U is the use we put ourselves to.
V is the valley we cut our roads through.
W is the woods we leave in the spring,
Now you've heard all that I'm going to sing.

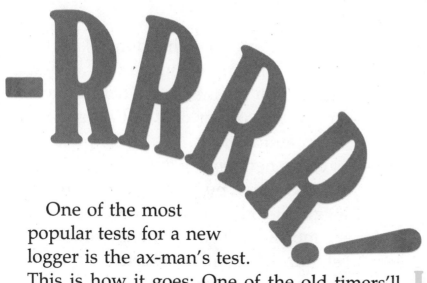

One of the most popular tests for a new logger is the ax-man's test. This is how it goes: One of the old timers'll get the ax and start chopping on the block. And he'll say, "Have you ever taken the ax-man's test?"

"No? All you've got to do is to hit the same spot on the chopping block four times in a row." Then he adds slyly, "With your eyes closed."

So the newcomer closes his eyes and takes one swing and then takes another. And he feels like he's coming pretty close to the same spot. He's trying hard to do it right. But the old-timers are up to mischief. They slip the newcomer's gloves or his hat on the chopping block, right where his ax is hitting. Of course he ruins his gloves or his hat and the old-timers go wild. They usually talk and tease about it for weeks.

There's another way they have of showing a new man that he still has a lot to learn. They send him after a "sky hook" or a "board

adapted from the
Archives of Northwest Folklore

shift
group of workers
who work
during the same
period of time

stretcher" or other things that don't exist. Or maybe they'll ask him to climb a tree at least ninety feet tall on his first day. That's quite a feat—but the newcomer dare not refuse. He has to "grin and bear" it. That's the price he pays for being new on the job.

As one old-timer put it, "The best thing about logging is that you are out in the fresh air every morning. When it rains, you're in the fresh air. Sometimes when it snows, you're in the fresh air too. You work as much as you can in the winter. It's better than the summer.

"In rainy weather you wear 'tin' pants and a 'tin' coat. The cloth is called 'tin' because it's heavy and almost waterproof.

"In summer when the weather gets hot, you work a 'hoot-owl' shift. You start work at daybreak and stop in early afternoon.

"Every time you cut down a tree, you should plant one. Or else you'd run out of trees some day. Little trees should be left standing. First, you should be cutting down trees that are dead, or dying. Leave the live ones till last."

Loggers like to make up funny names for their food. Flapjacks or pancakes are called *hot boys*. Tea is known as *belly wash* and coffee as *swamp water*.

There are a lot of jokes about loggers. Here is one that has been around a long time:

A guy had a million dollars he was going to give away. And he was looking for somebody to give it to. And so he found someone who owned a service station. And he walked up to him, and he said, "Hey, what would you do if I gave you a million dollars?" The service station owner said, "Oh, I'd get a string of service stations from coast to coast and multiply that million dollars by ten."

And the guy thought about it and said, "Well, you're kinda greedy. I'll look around some more."

Then he found someone who owned a restaurant and said, "Well, what would you do if I gave you a million dollars?"

And the restaurant owner said, "Well, I'd build a string of restaurants from coast to coast and multiply that million dollars by ten."

He said, "Well, you're a little greedy, too. I'll just look around a little more. I'll let you know."

He was drivin' down the road, and he saw a logger walkin' along carryin' his clothes and everythin' and stopped and said, "Hey, you look like an honest hard-working man. What would you do if I gave you a million dollars?"

The logger looked at him and said, "Well, I'd probably just keep on loggin' till it was all gone."

WOODS WORDS

reprinted from a book by
Walter F. McCulloch

A raft of—a whole lot of anything

Backin' the breeze—talking so much that the wind blows backward

Backs up to the window for his paycheck—does so little work he's ashamed to take the pay

Bait can—a lunch bucket

Ballix—any kind of messed-up situation

Balloon it—to pack up and leave camp

Barbed-wire deal—a tough situation to handle

Bark eater—a logger or a sawmill worker

Logger's can opener—an ax

Logging timber—trees big enough to cut down

Long Johns—heavy wool underwear with long sleeves and legs

Looking for a stretcher ride—working carelessly on the job

Loud talk him—to argue a man out of something

Low bore—a poor logger

Low man on the totem pole—the man with the poorest job in camp

Lump it off—to make a guess as to the amount of timber on a given piece of ground

Lye—poor coffee

Timber-rrrr!

Thinking About the Story

1. What is the ax-man's test? Why did the old-timers put new loggers through this test?

2. What is a "hoot-owl" shift? Why do loggers work "hoot-owl" shifts only in the summer?

3. It's important for a logger to plant a tree every time he cuts one down. Why? Why should little trees be left standing?

4. Reread pages 88–89. What kind of person might want to become a logger?

Doing Things

1. *Backin' the breeze, bait can, bark eater,* and *looking for a stretcher ride* are woods words. (See page 90.) Write a story about a logger using as many woods words as you can.

2. Paper is made from wood. Make a list of all the uses we have for paper. What would a modern society do without paper?

People at Work

Things To Do: Have a career day at your school. Find out about a job that interests you and share the information with your classmates.

Pineapple harvester on a large Hawaiian plantation.

Machine picking concord grapes, Yakima Valley, Washington.

Cantaloupe pickers, Imperial Valley, California.

A timber storage pond near Tacoma, Washington.

Indians dipnetting salmon, Oregon.

National park ranger.

93

Rounding up sheep, southern California.

Ulupalakua Ranch is on the slopes of Haleakala Crater which dominates Maui.

Workers on the Alaskan pipeline.

94

Chinese merchant, Chinatown, San Francisco, California.

Construction workers on the Grand Coulee Dam, Washington.

Postmaster with dog team meeting a mail plane in Alaska.

PALOMO AND FELIPE

J. A. Rickard

Storytelling was common entertainment on the trail into the new country. Travelers shared their experiences with one another, sometimes true tales, sometimes tall tales. And sometimes they told tales remembered from childhood. Here is a childhood tale from Old Mexico that was sometimes heard "on the trail." It is still being told in Mexican-American communities.

Everyone in the small town knew little Felipe and his donkey, Palomo. Palomo pulled a cart. Felipe was his driver. In the summer they carried water from the river to those who needed it. Sometimes they hauled wood from the forest nearby. The master lived in a big house near the river.

Felipe took care of Palomo and several other donkeys the master owned. He liked Palomo best of all the donkeys. Maybe that was because Palomo was the oldest one. Even when Palomo was lazy, Felipe never beat him with a stick. If there was extra corn or hay, Palomo always got it.

Palomo liked Felipe, too. Whenever he saw Felipe coming, he flapped his long ears and hee-hawed.

One morning the master sat in the plaza, talking to some friends. The little boy and the donkey passed by with their cart.

"There goes the most truthful person who ever worked for me," said the master.

"That boy always obeys. And he will not lie about anything."

"Ho! Ho!" laughed one of the master's friends. "He loves that donkey more than anything else. He would lie and disobey you, too, if it would help Palomo."

"I'll bet forty bushels of corn that he would not do either."

So the bet was made, and the master called the boy. "Felipe, you are my most trusted and honest worker. And I have told my friends that you will always do whatever I command. Am I right?"

"Yes," said Felipe.

"Now, I am going to ask you to do something that will be hard for you. Palomo is too old to work. I want you to sell him by tomorrow, Felipe."

Felipe was sad. He wanted to obey the master, but he wanted to keep Palomo, too. All afternoon he thought about what to do. At first he thought of telling the master that he had killed Palomo. But the master might ask, "Where is his body?" Felipe did not like that

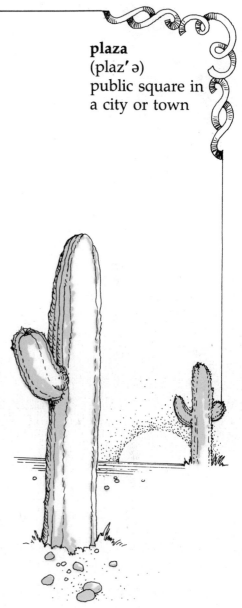

plaza
(plaz′ə)
public square in a city or town

97

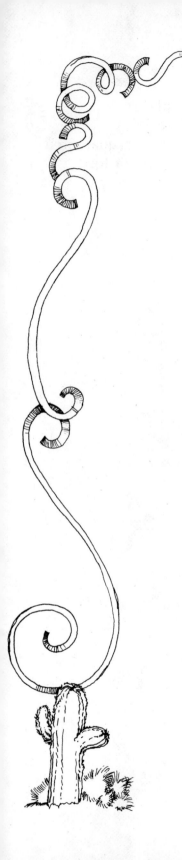

story. He couldn't really kill his faithful donkey anyway.

Then he thought he might say that the donkey had been stolen. But no thief would steal the oldest donkey and leave the others. Besides, the master had told his friends that Felipe was always honest. No, he just couldn't lie to the master.

Finally, Felipe asked his mother to help him with this problem. Soon they had worked out a plan.

The next morning Felipe and Palomo started out with their cart as usual. On the road they met the master.

"Good morning," said Felipe. "I have sold Palomo."

"But where is the money?" the master asked.

"Here it is. Five pesos," answered Felipe.

"But why is Palomo here with you? Why isn't he with his new owner?"

"Because I am his new owner. That money is what I have saved. And I have used it to buy Palomo from you."

Then the master laughed loudly. He had been right. Felipe had not lied. Yet he had obeyed him. And he still had Palomo. The master gave Felipe's money back to him and told the boy to keep on driving the donkey.

Felipe and Palomo were very happy.

Skills

Palomo and Felipe

Thinking About the Story

1. Felipe obeyed the master and told the truth. If Felipe had been different, how might the story have turned out?

2. The master trusted Felipe. If the master had been different, how might the story have turned out?

3. One lesson in the story is *treat animals well.* Why was this an important lesson in Old Mexico? Why is it still important?

4. What do you learn from the story about life in Old Mexico? Here are some questions to think about: What kinds of jobs did people have? How did people get food, water, and energy? What kinds of transportation did they have?

Doing Things

This story would make a good play. The main characters are Felipe, the master, and the master's friends. And don't forget Palomo who flapped his long ears and hee-hawed every time he saw Felipe!

Helmer Lindstrom:

adapted
from *North Coast
Folklife Festival*

Fisher and
Boat Carpenter

Helmer Lindstrom has spent his whole life on the north coast of Oregon. His father was also a fisher and boat builder in this area.

My father was quite a boat builder himself. I started the year I got married, in 1929. I changed boats around, makin' them longer, makin' them wider, and makin' them higher.

Wooden boats are goin' to the wayside like wooden ships, you know. In the old days it was iron men and wooden ships. Now it's wooden men and iron ships. We're in a fast-changin' world. We had linen nets in those days. Now they have fine nylon nets. They last better. They fish better.

Oh, no, you don't go back to the old. Everybody is progressin'. You can't beat advancement. Advancement is the spice of life. Keep goin' ahead. Don't go backwards.

I tried to talk my youngest son out of goin' into gill-net fishin'. And he said, "You know I like the water, and as long as I can make a livin', I'll stay with it." You can't argue with a person that's gettin' enjoyment out of what he's doin'.

We used to fish much more. Now we get about sixty to sixty-five days a year, or less. We're fishin' now where there is a lot of fish. We're takin' the best, the cream. You can't be a full-time fisher anymore.

This net I'm workin' on right now fishes about thirty-five feet deep. The salmon tangle themselves up, and that's why it's called gill-nettin'. When they move, the net has to be drawn up so it tightens out. That's how to catch them. But if they don't move, you don't get them.

Everybody likes to go fishin'. Know what the barber told me the other day? Don't put a sign in the window, "Home Sick," he said. Just put a sign on the door, "Gone Fishing," and everybody's happy.

spice of life
something that adds excitement, interest, or pleasure to everyday living

Felisa and the Tikling Bird

Jodi Parry Belknap

**sampaguita,
plumeria,
gardenia**
(sahm' pa gē' tə)
(plu' mer ē ə)
(gär dē' nyə)
types of flowers

lei
(lā)
wreath of
flowers to be
worn around the
head or neck

"Felisa! Come help me," called Mother. "Hurry! Tomorrow is the fiesta." Pink plumeria, pale yellow sampaguita, and buds of white gardenias were on the table behind her. They were ready to be strung into leis.

"Felisa, come here! Oh, where is that girl?"

Felisa was much too sad to answer her mother's call. She got up from the porch step and limped toward the street.

She was barely out of the yard when she heard her sister call. "Felisa, I need your help with my new dress."

Felisa did not answer Maria.

Her two brothers raced past her. They were practicing for the palo sebo. That's the boy's greased pole contest at the fiesta.

"Mateo! Juan! Wait for me," Felisa called. But they didn't.

Tears filled Felisa's eyes.

"Felisa, why do you cry?" said Grandma, coming up the path. "What do you want?

adapted from *Felisa and the Magic Tikling Bird*, by Jodi Parry Belnap, © 1973, Island Heritage Books, Honolulu, Hawaii.

Come. We make sweet things for the fiesta. You can help me make candy. Come along."

Felisa liked Grandma. In her bag were many good things—pili nuts, coconuts, bananas. As they walked back to the house, Grandma asked, "Why don't you help make things for the fiesta, Felisa?"

"I want to dance, Grandma. I want to dance the Tinikling for the fiesta tomorrow. But how can I dance with my limp?"

Grandma wiped the tears off Felisa's face with her apron. Softly she said, "Maybe you can dance, Felisa. If you really want to dance, tonight we talk."

"Talk, Grandma? I want to dance! The fiesta is tomorrow."

"We try, Felisa. You see. Come, we must talk."

That night, after she and Grandma had talked it over, Felisa lay in bed thinking. She wondered if she really would be able to dance tomorrow. Maybe, she thought. Just maybe.

In the moonlight outside her window was the shadowy form of a strange old bird.

"Ti-kling! Ti-kling! Tap! Tap! Tap!"

Felisa looked out the window, wondering if she was awake or asleep. "Who are you?" she asked.

In the yard stood a tall old bird with a long twisty neck, fuzzy feathers, and the crookedest, spindliest legs she had ever seen. In fact, his legs were crooked, so *very* crooked, that Felisa just stared.

The bird hopped up and down.

"Who are you?" Felisa asked again.

"Ti-kling! Ti-kling! I am the Tikling bird," he clacked. "I am the best dancer in the whole world."

Felisa laughed out loud. "You? A dancer? With those crooked legs? I don't believe you. Crooked legs can't dance."

"Aaaaaaaaaaak! Crooked legs *can* dance, Felisa. Come, I will teach you! But you must pay whatever I ask."

"I cannot give you anything, Mr. Bird," said Felisa, her voice shaking. "I have nothing. We are poor."

"Oh, but you do, Felisa," croaked the bird. "You have so much to give. Just wait and see."

As he spoke, five birds appeared carrying a banduria, a laud, a guitar, and bamboo poles.

"Watch me, Felisa!" commanded the Tikling bird. "I'll show you how it's done."

Clack! clack! clack! went the bamboo poles as they were held and snapped together by a pair of birds seated on the ground. Slowly at first, then faster! faster! in time with the music! The Tikling bird danced in and out of

bamboo
(bam bü')
type of grass
with a tall, stiff,
hollow stem

the clacking bamboo poles. He was moving so fast that his legs escaped being caught by the poles. His crooked legs were a blur.

"Come, Felisa. Come, Little Crooked Legs. Come dance with me."

Taking hold of his wing tip, her eyes wide, Felisa began to dance. Slowly, clumsily, awkwardly, she stepped in and out of the clacking poles. As the clacking grew faster, she jumped higher and faster than ever before.

Clack! clack! clack! Lesson followed lesson. She sang and laughed and danced so gaily that the bird's heart was filled with happiness.

"Good. Very good!" said the Tikling bird. "Now you must pay."

"Oh!" gasped Felisa. "I have no money. I told you before. I have nothing to give."

"Yes, you have something to give. Give your heart to everything you do. Will you make that promise, Felisa?"

"Yes, Mr. Bird. I promise! I promise!"

"Felisa!" It was her mother's voice. "Hurry! We have much to do. It is a beautiful day for the fiesta."

Felisa dressed and ran to the kitchen to help her mother.

Outside, her father was busy with Mateo and Juan. They were loading the truck. Hearing Felisa's giggling, Father called, "Hurry now, Felisa. We'll be late. I want everyone to see that I've got the best family at the fiesta today."

Grandma was in the kitchen. Her arms were filled with boxes of freshly made bucayo. She leaned over and whispered, "You have one pretty smile, Felisa."

"Mabuhay! Mabuhay! Ladies and gentlemen!"

Words boomed from a loudspeaker. Booths bulged with rich foods. The air was filled with the sweet smell of sampaguita and plumeria.

bucayo
(bü′kĭ yō)
coconut candy

mabuhay
(mah′boo hī)
special greeting
to someone you
are very fond of

106

People in gaily colored costumes were everywhere.

"Mabuhay!" said the Master of Ceremonies. "We are ready for the first event of the day, the palo sebo contest for our young boys. This will be followed by the Queen contest, and then the children's dances. Enjoy yourselves. It is a beautiful day for a fiesta!"

Felisa cheered when Mateo and Juan tried to climb the greased pole in the palo sebo contest. She watched with pride as the banner of a Queen's attendant was pinned on her sister, Maria.

Then it was time for the children's folk dances.

The stage for the dancing shimmered in the afternoon sunlight. Three musicians appeared. They carried their instruments.

Felisa trembled. But she took her place in the line of dancers.

The musicians began to play. Clack! clack! clack! sounded the bamboo poles.

Suddenly Felisa was on the stage. Clack! clack! clack! She was shaking. She wanted to turn back.

Clack! clack! clack! went the beak of the Tikling bird. "You can do it if you try, Felisa," he said. "Remember your promise. Dance with all your heart."

Clack, clack, clack. The poles snapped together.

Clack, clack, clack. One, two, three. One, two, three. Faster and faster the musicians played.

Sam-pa-gi ta't kam-pu-pot
May gan-da't-a-lin-dog.
Mag-sa-yaw sa sa-liw ng tug-tu-gin.
Faster and faster they sang the Tinikling.

Felisa hopped in and out, across and between, first one foot and then the other. Faster and faster the poles went, until she couldn't see them at all.

Hu-mak-bang, hu-mak-bang
Ng hak-bang ti-ni-kling.
The music stopped. The dance was over.

Grandma's eyes filled with tears. "Felisa danced!" she whispered.

"Felisa," her father shouted happily, "you danced!"

And Maria and Juan and Mateo and Mother beamed.

That night before bed, Felisa sat alone for a long time. The night was silent except for the sound of a dog somewhere far away. Shadows danced outside in the moonlight.

Climbing into bed, she closed her eyes and listened as long as she could. Then, with a smile on her face, Felisa fell asleep.

Felisa and the Tikling Bird

Thinking About the Story

1. This is a Filipino tale. Why do you think the author uses Hawaii as the setting for this story?

2. Reread pages 102–103. Why do you think Felisa was sad?

3. What lesson did Felisa learn from the Tikling Bird? What did Felisa have to pay for the lesson?

4. Reread pages 103–104. Who was speaking to Felisa? Was it really the Tikling Bird or was Felisa dreaming? Give reasons for your answer.

Doing Things

1. Tinikling is a fairly easy dance to learn. Find out how to dance the Tinikling from your gym teacher or from a book on folk dancing. You can substitute broom sticks for bamboo poles if necessary. Your class will enjoy a Tinikling demonstration.

2. Some festivals celebrate the harvest. Some celebrate the coming of spring. Others recall a special historical or religious event. What is your favorite festival? What does it celebrate? Are there any special dances, songs, parades, foods, or displays during the celebration? Plan a class festival day.

Walt Disney: Man of Imagination (1901–1966)

Walt Disney's magic touches the young-of-heart everywhere. He never lost the feel of being a child. "Adults are only kids grown up," he often said.

Walt Disney's first Mickey Mouse cartoon was released in 1928. Mickey became an overnight star. "You can't help liking him," said movie-goers around the world.

Then came "Snow White and the Seven Dwarfs" in 1937. It was Walt Disney's first full-length animated cartoon. Like Mickey Mouse, this film was an instant success.

Besides making motion pictures, Walt Disney produced the "Mickey Mouse Club" for television. It was on the air five days a week for years. Millions and millions of children watched it regularly. He also produced a special evening TV series. Besides the children, millions of adults enjoyed the programs.

But Walt Disney did much more. He built two "Disneylands" of make-believe, one in California, the other in Florida.

"I want Disneyland and Walt Disney World to be places where parents and children can have fun together."

SOMETHING TO BRAG ABOUT

Conversation with a Mosquito

Onto a boy's arm came a mosquito.
"Don't hit! Don't hit!" it hummed.
  "Grandchildren have I to sing to."
"Imagine," the boy said.
  "So small and yet a grandfather."

Eskimo poem
collected by James Houston

California Earthquake Lore

collected by
Carey McWilliams

The Pacific States are record-breakers without even trying. . . .

Everything on the Pacific seems to grow bigger, wider, colder, hotter than anywhere else.

For example, during an earthquake in California . . .

A hen laid three eggs in a few moments after the first shock was felt.

A car on Long Beach Boulevard shook so hard that it lost all four tires.

As you can see, tall tales grow taller in the Pacific States too. Hathaway Jones and Benjamin Franklin Finn are two tall-tale tellers of the old frontier. Their names are still remembered. They grew famous spinning their yarns.

"A cat can find its claws when it has to climb a tree."

—Finnish proverb from Oregon

Arthur Belnap tells this one about his grandfather, Benjamin Franklin Finn:

He had bees, you know. That was down on the old Finn place. He was a great one to go out and find a tree full of honey. One time he found a bee tree and crawled in to eat the honey. He ate so much he couldn't get back out of the tree. So he had to go home and get an ax and chop himself out.

Here is one of Hathaway Jones' best tales:

One year the huckleberry crop on the Rogue River was so heavy with fruit, the bushes sagged. In the woods the blue kind were almost as large as cherries. So one morning Hathaway Jones decided he would pick a few and make a pie or two. He wandered up the mountainside in back of his cabin. He picked a few here and a few there. He didn't care at all how long it would take to fill his pail.

Now it happened that very morning that a bear was in the same spot filling his stomach with those blue huckleberries. They met on opposite sides of a bush. Both were very surprised. Hathaway was unarmed. So he spoke to the bear and tipped his hat to him. Then he tried all the other things he could remember that are supposed to cause wild animals to go

Hathaway Jones and the Flying Bear

collected by
Stephen Dow Beckham

away and leave folks alone. The bear, however, did not seem to take to the idea. Instead of walking away with his tail between his legs, he gave a mean growl and charged.

Hathaway ran. The bear kept up a pace that made Hathaway work harder and harder. Everything, however, would have ended all right. But Hathaway came to a very high place.

The bear by now was right behind him. So Hathaway climbed a tall, slim fir tree. The bear climbed the tree, too. Up they went. They got so high the tree began to bend. Soon, with Hathaway right in the tip-top, the tree bent so far he jumped out. Free of his weight, the tree snapped back. It threw the bear far out into the air and a mile across the canyon. There he landed in another tall, slim fir tree.

The tree swayed back from the weight of the sudden force. Then it whipped forward and threw the bear across the canyon back into the first tree. Then away he went and then back again on another trip. Hathaway just sat down and watched him on his flying trip. In the air, the bear stretched out his neck and spread his legs like a flying squirrel.

Finally Hathaway tired of watching the bear flying through the air like an acrobat. He fetched an ax from his cabin. And, while the critter was flying, he chopped down the young fir tree. The tree fell when the bear was about halfway back on the return trip. Seeing the tree gone, the bear changed its course. It landed in a larger tree, off to one side.

The larger tree was much stronger than the tree Hathaway had cut down. It threw the bear clear over the top of the small tree he had been using on the other side. He landed in a still larger and stronger tree. That tree threw the bear back way over the top of the big tree on Hathaway's side into a still larger and stronger tree. And so on, back and forth. Each trip the bear chose a taller and stronger tree. Finally, passing through the air, he looked no bigger than a mouse. Then, at last, an extra big tree on Hathaway's side threw the bear clear over the top of the mountain. The mountain was 4,000 feet high.

A stranger, standing around the Post Office in Agnes, Oregon, heard Hathaway tell this experience. The stranger practically told him he was a liar. Hathaway looked the stranger over, shook his head, and then with patience, answered. "Wouldn't expect a tenderfoot to believe me. But I can take you to the young fir tree I chopped down. What better proof would a man of sense want?"

tenderfoot
(ten′ dər füt′)
newcomer

SARAH ROYCE: Diary of a Pioneer Woman

Sarah Royce was one of many brave pioneers who dared the dangerous journey west to California. With her husband and small daughter, she left her friends in the East in 1848. They reached Iowa and lived there until spring. In late April, 1849, they began their journey to California. The journey ended six months later.

Like many others, Sarah Royce faced stampedes, starvation, thirst, hostile Indians, exhaustion, and disease.

Here is some of what she said in her diary about the trip:

Plains

April 30, 1849. We began our journey to California from Iowa. Our outfit consisted of a covered wagon loaded with provisions for sleeping, cooking, etc. Our wagon was drawn by three yoke of oxen and the one yoke of cows. We planned to use their milk for food.

I seated myself in the wagon. My little two-year-old Mary was placed beside me. My hus-

stampede
(stam pēd′)
sudden rush or flight of a frightened herd of cattle, horses, etc.

yoke
(yōk)
wooden frame that fits around the necks of two work animals to fasten them together for pulling a plow or vehicle

118

band and the other man of our little company started the team.

Our first noon lunch was eaten by the whole party, seated in front of the wagon. The cattle grazed nearby. After a short rest we again moved on. The afternoon wore away quietly. Night was coming on. No house was within sight.

Why did I look for one? I knew we were to camp. But surely there would be a few trees or a sheltering hill where we could stop our wagon. No, only the level prairie stretched on each side of the way. I saw no cozy nook. I had thought about this for many months. But now I was faced with the reality. There would be no house or home to shelter us and our baby girl.

And this was to be the same for many weeks, perhaps months.

Beginning of June. An enemy, unseen, was advancing upon us. Our wagon was his first point of attack.

The oldest man (*from the company they had joined*) complained of pain and sickness. He was forced to lie down in the wagon. He used the bed near where Mary and I sat. He shook terribly. The captain was called. Medicine brought some relief.

Two riders appeared. They let us know that a doctor was with their group two miles away.

cholera
(kol′ ər ə)
serious disease
of the stomach
or intestines

disinfect
(dis′in fekt′)
to destroy
disease germs

quicksand
(kwik′ sand′)
very deep, soft,
wet sand that
will not hold up
a person's
weight

current
(kėr′ ənt)
flow of water;
running stream

We made the sick man comfortable and went on. The doctor said it was Asiatic Cholera. Within three hours the poor old man had died.

Now we had to disinfect the wagon and everything in it. That night we camped out in a tent. I refused to lie down. For there was only room and covering for one beside Mary. My husband had been on guard the night before and was exhausted. I insisted that he rest. I sat by my little one, leaning my head on her pillow, and tried to sleep.

Morning came at last.

Then came the work of cleaning the wagon, washing bed clothes, and sunning and airing everything.

June 16. We arrived at the crossing of Loup Fork of the Platte River. Here we found two other companies waiting for the waters to go down. The bed of the Loup is, for miles, formed of quicksand. So where teams might cross in safety one day, there might be deep holes the next. This was especially true after the waters had been swollen by heavy rains as had lately been the case. A man had drowned only a short time before our arrival.

On the third day, it was announced the water was gentle enough for us to try to pass. But there was still an ugly current near the farther shore. On our side there was shallow water for a distance. Then there was an island of sand. After that the current was deep and strong. So the teams would have to be doubled, and long ropes used. And we would have to hurry. For the river bottom shifted every hour or so.

One team at a time crossed quickly to the island. I sat beside my little Sarah. We felt the wagon trembling under us, as in an earthquake. The shaking did not stop while we stopped on the island. Then men and cattle worked nobly. In due time we were west of Loup Fork.

June 20. I was awakened between three and four o'clock in the morning by the sound of rain upon the wagon-top. It was a quiet shower. Then a flash of lightning came. It was followed in a moment by a strange rushing sound. Quickly it became as loud as thunder. The wagon began to shake violently. It was pushed sideways by a great force. Then it was lifted and thrown violently over on its side. There was a crash of breaking wheels and chains. Then I heard the rapid tramp of cattle. Then quiet again. . . .

But now what was to be done? None of us were hurt much. But the cattle had stampeded and were all gone. How, and when could we get them? In such cases, they often ran themselves to death. Some of the men, we

blacksmith
person who
mends tools and
shoes horses

were told, had mounted horses and were already chasing them. But those broken wheels—how could they be repaired? It soon turned out there was a blacksmith in the company. He had tools and a few odd pieces of wood. There were also two families who had brought with them wide, hardwood boards. They'd used them for tables while camping. In a few hours, the lost cattle were all recovered. Mending the wagons took two days. . . .

July 4. In the morning, we passed some remarkable rocks called Ancient Bluff Ruins *(probably Court House Rock)*. Soon we sighted Chimney Rock. It is a huge natural tower. It could be seen for many miles.

That afternoon we stopped to celebrate Independence Day. In one tent, a few gathered for a dance. In another, several of us enjoyed a cheerful "sing."

We were now within a hundred miles of Fort Laramie.

Desert

(The Royce party decided against waiting for the rest of the company to go the "new southern route." They prepared to follow the Great Salt Lake west along the Humboldt River and Carson Desert to the Sierra Mountains. They left Salt Lake City at the end of August.)

October 3. Day dawned. We began to look anxiously for signs to mark the Sink of the Humboldt. But it was nearly noonday before we came to them. We had been told that two or three miles past the Sink we should look for the road to the left. We did look, and kept looking, and going on. The sun got lower and lower. The night was fast approaching. Now we understood. We had missed the road. Now we were miles out on the desert without a mouthful of food for the cattle. We had only two or three quarts of water.

What could we do but stop?

The first question in the morning was, "How can we keep the oxen from starving?" A happy thought occurred.

We had managed to keep something in the shape of a bed to sleep on. It was a mattress tick. Just before leaving Salt Lake we had put some fresh hay into it. The old gentleman traveling with us also had a small straw mattress. The two together might keep the poor things from starving for a few hours. Two or three quarts of water in our little cask would only last a few hours. For myself, I decided to take scarcely any of it. For I had found that I could do with less drink than most land travelers. . . .

Should we go on? Here we were, without water and only a few mouthfuls of poor feed.

sink
basin; all the land drained by a river and the streams that flow into it

cask
barrel

Our animals were already tired out and very hungry and thirsty. No, it would be madness to go farther out in the desert.

So there was nothing to be done but to turn back and try to find the meadows. Turn back! What a chill the words sent through me. *Turn back,* on a journey like that. . . .

I had now become so impressed with the danger of the cattle giving out that I refused to ride. I left the wagon and walked. . . .

Mountains

(The Royce Party had reached the Sierra Nevada range. There was already snow in the ravines. Only haste and good fortune could save them. They pressed on. A government relief company found them in the mountains

meadow
(med' ō)
piece of grassy
land

and provided mules to carry them through the steepest parts.)

October 17. I had not ridden horseback for several years. And, whenever I had, it had been side-saddle. Now I was to have a Spanish saddle. I must also have Mary in front of me. . . .

At the head of Carson Valley we entered the great canyon. The road because so rough and steep I had difficulty holding Mary and keeping my seat. The men had hard work to drive the cattle and mules.

There were often boulders at the crossing of the streams. Sometimes the trail seemed to disappear between great masses of rock. As the canyon narrowed, the rocky walls were almost straight up and down.

The days were shortening fast. The animals became more and more difficult to manage as the way became rougher.

October 19. That night we slept within a few yards of snow. Water froze in our pans not far from the fire. But the morning was bright. And that day we were to cross the highest ridge and view the "promised land." Soon we would begin our climb down into warmth and safety. . . .

California, land of sunny skies—that was my first look into your smiling face. I loved you from that moment. You seemed to welcome me with a loving look into rest and safety.

Josiah Royce was Sarah Royce's fourth child and only son. Born in California, he spent his childhood there on his parents' farm near Green Valley. Later he became one of the best known thinkers that frontier California had produced.

While a teacher at Harvard, Josiah was asked to write a history of the early days in California. For his use, Sarah Royce wrote this account based on her journal. The account was written more than thirty years after she came west.

**Sarah Royce:
Diary of a Pioneer Woman**

Thinking About the Story

1. Sarah Royce and her family went to Iowa. They waited until spring before going farther west. Why did they stop in Iowa?

2. Reread pages 119–120. Who was the unseen enemy that Sarah spoke of? Whom did the enemy attack? How did they defend against this enemy?

3. When the wagon wheels broke, who fixed them? Where did the spare parts come from?

4. The pioneers depended on the animals, especially horses and oxen. Why? Find examples from the story that show how important the animals were.

Doing Things

1. In this story we learn what a trip west was like for a pioneer woman. What did Mr. Royce do during the trip? How was it the same and different for the two parents? What was it like for little Mary?

2. What did the Royce family take with them on the trip west? If you were planning a 3,000-mile trip to California today, what would you take along? What if you were going by car? by plane? by train? by bicycle? Then what would you take?

Pacific States: Hall of Fame

Mary Ellen Pleasant (1814–1904)
Californian. Civil rights activist.

Ronald Reagan (1911–)
Fortieth President of the
United States.

*Things To Do: Make up
a Hall of Fame
bulletin board for
your classroom.
Everyone should
nominate one person to
be included. Find or
make up pictures,
stories, poems, songs,
and photographs.*

Isadora Duncan (1878–1927)
Californian. Dancer, known for
interpretive and barefoot
dancing.

Abigail Scott Duniway (1834–1915) Oregonian. Started a newspaper, *The New Northwest,* in 1871 and campaigned for women's right to vote.

George Washington Bush (1791–1867) Oregonian. Pioneer settler in Oregon Territory.

Chief Joseph (1840–1904) Oregonian. A Nez Percé Indian chief.

"Never sell the bones of your father."

—Chief Joseph

William O. Douglas (1898–1980) Washingtonian. U.S. Supreme Court Justice.

Dixy Lee Ray (1914—) Washingtonian. Former Governor.

Howard Rock (1911–1976) Alaskan. Eskimo journalist. Founding editor, *Tundra Times,* first native Alaskan newspaper.

Emily Ivanoff Brown (1907—) Alaskan. Elementary school teacher, nurse, collector of traditional Eskimo folklore.

Kamehameha the Great (1758–1819) Hawaiian Islands Chief. United all eight islands.

Queen Liliuokalani (1838–1917) Hawaiian. Hawaii's last queen.

Other Famous People from the Pacific States

California
Pio Pico, first Black governor of California, 1845–46
Joseph Paul DiMaggio, baseball Hall of Famer
John Steinbeck, writer

Oregon
Marcus and Narcissa Whitman, pioneer settlers
Mason Williams, composer

Washington
Harry Lillis "Bing" Crosby, singer
Patrice Munsel, opera singer

Alaska
James Wickersham, judge, educator, writer
Roxanne "Roxie" Brooks, championship dogmusher

Hawaii
Ka'ahumanu, queen, increased island's literacy rate
George R. Ariyoshi, governor
John Anthony Burns, policeman, governor, and congressional delegate

Paul Bunyan in Puget Sound

Dell J. McCormick

One day Paul Bunyan thought his ox
    Was going to up and die,
So he picked up a pick and a spade
    And a tear drop filled his eye.

And sadly by the sea he dug
    A deep hole in the ground,
But Babe got well. The sea surged in.
    The hole is Puget Sound.

Harold W. Felton

sound
inlet or arm of
the sea

Paul Bunyan is one of the country's big folk heroes. Paul Bunyan was not a real person. He was invented by writers. Tales of him pop up in Texas, in Wisconsin, and, of course, in the Pacific States.

When he was digging the Sound, Paul hitched Babe, his blue ox, to a giant scoop shovel and started to work. The first load of dirt was so big, people didn't want it dumped on their land. So Paul had to haul it way back in the mountains. He dumped it in two piles. By the time the Sound was completed, the piles of dirt were so high they could be seen for miles. They named these piles Mt. Rainier and Mt. Baker. They are still there to this day.

harbor
(här′bər)
sheltered area of
deep water for
ships and boats

channel
(chan′l)
bed of a stream,
or river

Paul ran into trouble from the start. Everyone wanted the Sound to run in different directions. The folks from Tacoma wanted it to go their way. Then someone near Everett wanted a harbor there. It kept Paul hopping trying to satisfy them all. That's the reason the Sound has so many twists and turns. When Paul was almost through, he remembered his promise to dig a harbor for some folks to the south. So he scooped out Hood Canal.

Finally the Sound was completed. Everyone was pleased. Paul told his friend, Peter Puget, to arrange for a big celebration. They would name it "Puget Sound" on that day. Of course Peter Puget was very proud that the Sound was to be named after him. He spent a lot of time getting everything ready. But the settlers had a secret meeting. They decided to name it "Whidby Sound." They even had maps printed with the name in big letters.

When Paul heard about it, he was pretty mad. So he just went out with his big shovel and started filling it all up again. In no time at all most of the channel was filled in. He stood there and threw in shovelful after shovelful of dirt. After that, there were almost a thousand islands dotting the Sound.

A group of settlers finally came to him and asked him to stop. They promised to change the name back to Puget Sound. They told him it was the fault of the people living on Whidby Peninsula. They were the ones who had decided to keep the name Whidby Sound. They didn't think Paul could do anything about the matter because the Sound had been completed.

"Let him fill up the Sound!" the people from Whidby Peninsula cried. "It won't matter. We can still haul our vegetables and milk to market along the roads."

Paul hated the way they had tricked his good friend Peter Puget. So he decided to make them pay for it. Well, Paul just took his ax and cut a notch in the land that connected Whidby Peninsula with the mainland. The water from the Sound rushed in and filled up the passage. The force of the water was so great that the tides made it almost impossible to cross, even in a boat. The Whidby people were now on an island cut off from the mainland. Their home has been known as Whidby Island ever since. The channel that Paul cut is filled with raging water to this day. It is known as "Deception Pass."

And that's how Paul Bunyan
and his blue ox Babe
made Puget Sound.

peninsula
(pə nin′sə lə)
piece of land almost surrounded by water

deception
(di sep′shən)
trick meant to fool

Tall Tale Sampler /
Paul Bunyan in Puget Sound

Thinking About the Story

1. What proof did Hathaway Jones give to show that the story of the flying bear was true? Do you think he had enough proof? Why or why not?

2. Compare this Hathaway Jones story with "Tangling with a Grizzly." (Use the Table of Contents to locate it.) In what ways are the stories the same? different?

3. What is the most amazing thing Paul Bunyan did in this story? What other amazing things could a "super logger" have done?

Doing Things

1. The story of "Hathaway Jones and the Flying Bear" may remind you of cartoons you have seen. Try drawing a comic strip about this tall tale.

2. Paul Bunyan is a lumberjack hero. Make up a modern tall tale about a construction worker. Or a ballet dancer. Or an acrobat. Or a cook. Or a doctor. Or a fisher. Tall tales usually begin with "an ounce of truth."

AGAYK AND THE MAGIC SPEAR

collected by I. G. Edmonds

The Eskimo shaman or medicine man is a person with special powers. These powers are often used to find whales or game animals when food is scarce. They are also used to cure sick people and to fight enemies. Shamans usually get their special powers through dreaming, singing, or carrying magical objects known as amulets.

In this story, the old man, Agayk, has special magic powers. As in most legends and folktales, the forces for good overcome the forces for bad.

shaman
(shä′mən)
priest with magic
power

ice pack
huge field or
sheet of ice

floe
(flō)
field or sheet of
floating ice

One terrible day when the earth was frozen the ground shook. The ice pack cracked on the sea. The floes piled up, grinding and crushing as the huge slabs of frozen ice heaved up on the shore.

The ice smashed the igloo houses of a little fishing village on the frozen shore. The frightened people fled. In their hurry they forgot Agayk, their medicine man, who was too old to run. That is, all forgot him except the boy, Niklik.

Niklik stayed with the old man. Somehow they missed death in the crushing ice. But when the earthquake was over, their troubles did not end.

There was nothing to eat. The polar bear, the seal, and even the fish in the sea had run away from the shaking earth even as the people did.

"Make the fish come back," Niklik said. "I am very hungry."

"That I cannot do," Agayk said sadly.

"But you are a great shaman," the boy said. "Don't the people say that a shaman can walk under the water and talk to the fish and whales?"

"The people say that—yes," Agayk replied. His tired old eyes looked sadly at the boy. "But that is a very difficult thing for me to do. I think we must cross the trail over the great ice mountain and fish in the other bay."

"It is so far. Magic is easier."

The magician's dark face looked sad.

"Yes," he said. "Once I was a great medicine man. I was a friend of Raven who flew to the sun and brought back the spark that made the first fire on earth. And I helped the great black bird with his medicine the day a great wave was going to sweep over the land. He turned this wave into Denali, the Great One."

He turned and pointed south at the frozen spire of the great mountain. Gold seekers would one day call it Mount McKinley.

"The great bird taught me much magic and medicine. But now I am old and weak. Only the young and strong can make great medicine. This is the way of the world. Raven grew old and left us. The same thing is happening to me."

"Then we will starve," the boy said sadly.

"No, there is fish across the mountains. It is a long way, but we can get there before we starve. Then we have only to cut a hole in the ice and drop in our ivory hooks."

"But the people of the bay are our great enemies," Niklik protested. "They will kill us if we try to fish in their water!"

"Not if we fight them with magic," Agayk replied.

"But you said you were too old to make medicine!"

"I am, but you are young," Agayk said. "You must make the magic."

"I don't know how," Niklik protested.

"I hope I have enough strength left to teach you. Are you willing to learn?"

"Oh, yes!" Niklik said. "Will I be able to walk under the sea and talk to fishes?"

"Well—no," Agayk said. "I am not strong enough to teach you that trick."

"Then maybe you can teach me how to

spire
(spīr)
pointed peak
such as a tower
or a steeple

ivory
(ī′ vər ē)
hard, white
substance
making up the
tusks of
elephants,
walruses, etc.

make a fog roll in from the Smokey Sea and hide us. Or will I be able to turn into Nanook, the bear, and frighten our enemies away?''

"I think the best I can do today is teach you to throw a magic spear."

"Oh, that will be wonderful!" Niklik cried.

"The spear will be made of words."

"Words?" Niklik said uneasily. "That is the strangest spear I ever heard of. Will it work?''

"Because things are as they are—yes, I think so," Agayk said. "Often there is more magic in words than in anything in the world. Had I known this when I was a young man, I would have been an even greater magician than I was."

And so the two climbed the icy trail over the mountain range. It took them five days without food, and they were very weak from hunger when they came to the other bay.

Niklik chopped a hole on the frozen sea, and dropped an ivory hook into the dark water.

It was night, for this was winter and the sun would not shine here above the Arctic Circle for two more months. But the stars were bright. The Northern Lights wove great curtains of soft green, pink, and blue colors through the sky. This made it as bright as twilight on the ice pack.

Arctic Circle
(ärk′ tik)
imaginary boundary of the north polar region

Northern Lights
streamers or bands of light appearing in the northern sky at night

In a short time, the people of the bay saw Niklik and Agayk. They grabbed their spears and hitched their sleds to dogteams. Then across the ice they came in a mad race to attack the boy and the old man.

"Aiee!" the old medicine man said. "The two in front must be Agarook and Attu. They are the mightiest hunters of this village. I have heard it said that they are very jealous of each other. Every time one does a mighty deed, the other will not sleep until he matches it. They are running a race now to see who will have the honor of killing us."

"Maybe you had better use the magic spear." Niklik said uneasily. "They look like very fierce men."

"They are," Agayk admitted, "but the spear would not be powerful enough in my old hands. These men know me. They know I am old and my power is gone. Only you can save us now, Niklik my son."

"Then give me the spear quickly!" the boy cried.

"The spear is only words. When the killers come, speak as I tell you."

The old medicine man told Niklik what to say. The boy listened, first in surprise and then in alarm.

"We are as good as dead," he said, almost weeping.

"Oh, no," Agayk insisted. "This is good

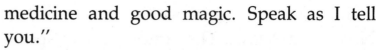

runner
either of the
narrow pieces on
which a sleigh or
sled slides
huskies
(hus′kēz)
any Arctic sled
dogs originating
in Siberia

medicine and good magic. Speak as I tell you."

The hunters were almost upon them. Niklik could hear the squeak of the ivory runners as the yelping huskies pulled the racing sleds across the ice pack.

Agayk pushed back the fur-trimmed hood of his parka so the two hunters could see his face.

"You are the old shaman from across the icy mountains," Agarook cried. "Why do you steal our fish?"

"Our fish ran when the earth shook," Agayk said.

"I will kill you for stealing our fish," Agarook said.

"No, I will kill them," Attu said jealously.

"Neither of you will kill us," Agayk said firmly. "We are protected by magic."

"You are old. Your magic is weak," Agarook said.

"That is true," Agayk agreed. "But the boy is young. He will save us with his magic."

The two jealous hunters looked at him in amazement. "The boy? Who ever heard of a boy medicine man!"

"You have heard of one for I have just told you," Agayk said firmly. "The boy is a great shaman. He has secret medicine, which will bring the seal from the sea and the bear in from the floes so they can be easily killed."

Attu pointed the ivory tip of his spear at Niklik's heart. "Tell me this secret or I will kill you!"

The boy trembled. His throat was dry with fear. He had trouble speaking the words that Agayk promised had magic hidden in them.

Finally he managed to say: "I can give the secret to only one of you. The secret can only be given to the mightiest hunter."

"I am the mightiest!" Attu cried.

"No!" Agarook shouted. "I am the greatest of all!"

"I'll show you who is mightiest!" Attu cried, raising his spear so it pointed at his enemy instead of the boy, Niklik. "Too long you have insulted me with your wild bragging, Agarook!"

"You are the braggart!" his jealous rival cried, raising his own spear.

All the hatred and jealousy of their years of rivalry boiled over. They started to fight, lunging at each other with their spears.

"Who will win?" Niklik asked Agayk.

"Neither," the old medicine man said. "Each is just as strong as the other. So both must win and both must lose."

"That can't be," Niklik said.

"We'll see," the old shaman said.

As he spoke, each man drove his spear into the other. Both men fell into the fish hole and disappeared under the sea.

braggart
(brag′ərt)
person who
brags; boaster

Soon the rest of the hunters came up. Surprised at finding the two great hunters gone, they asked where the two were. Agayk told them Niklik had killed them with his magic.

"If a boy can kill such mighty men that even we grown men fear to fight, it must be great magic indeed," their leader said.

"That is right," Agayk said. "He has a magic spear of words. He spoke them and they entered Agarook and Attu. In minutes both men were dead. Would you like him to speak the words to you?"

"Oh, no!" the others said.

"Then let us fish in your waters until the fish return to our own bay, and I will beg the boy to spare you."

The fearful villagers agreed.

That is how Niklik learned that there is magic in words. With Agayk as his teacher, he grew even wiser in the use of magic talk. So it was that he became a great and famous man among his people, the Eskimo.

"They told me stories which would create in me the desire to become brave and good and strong; to become a good speaker, a good leader, and they taught me to honor old people and to do all in my power to help them."

—Chief Shelton

Agayk and the Magic Spear

Thinking About the Story

1. Read page 137, paragraphs 1 and 2. What natural disaster is described in these paragraphs? Why are frozen slabs of ice sometimes dangerous in the Arctic?

2. Describe Agayk. Think about these questions: Was he confident that he and the boy would survive? Why didn't Agayk use his magic? What plan did he have instead?

3. Describe Niklik. Why did Niklik lack confidence in Agayk's plan? Find sentences in the story that tell how Niklik felt. Do you think Niklik was a coward?

4. Were Attu and Agarook stronger than Niklik and Agayk? What was Agayk's spear made of? Why was it stronger than Attu's and Agarook's spears? What lesson does this story teach about strength? about magic?

5. In the story, the spear tips and the runners on the sleds were made of ivory. Where do you think the ivory came from?

Doing Things

The sun does not shine in the Arctic Circle during the winter months. Find out more about the seasons in "the land of the midnight sun." Make a report to your class.

Tall Talk

Pacific States "Chin Music"
collected by Alvin Schwartz

Do you like *waggin' your chin*? You might want to get some of this Pacific States "chin music" (tall talk) into your *knowledge box*.

cook—*bean master*
biscuits—*snowballs*
onions—*skunk eggs*
sweet potatoes—*music roots*
friend—*old socks*
graveyard—*bone orchard*
head—*knowledge box*
mouth—*dining room*
talking a lot—*waggin' your chin*

Brags

In eastern Oregon the wind blows so hard that cattle have to stand on their hay to keep it from blowing away.

Oregon

Everybody wants to live in California. So new towns pop up fast. The train companies keep a man on the rear platform just to write down the names of the towns that spring up after the train goes by.

Maria Leach, California

A man at Shilshoe Bay Marina claims to have caught two fish on one hook. "The first fish that grabbed the bait was a five-pound rock fish. Then a thirty-pound cod got hold of the rock fish. The rock fish was so spiney that once the cod bit in, it couldn't get its mouth free."

Thomas H. Spencer, Washington

One Alaskan said: "It gets so cold where I live that our words freeze coming out of our mouths. We have to throw them into the frying pan and thaw them out to know what we're talking about."

Alaska

LAZY COYOTE

collected by Ray Raphael

Stories about clever characters, or tricksters, were favorites among the American Indians. Different tribes have different tricksters. Coyote was one of many animal characters used by storytellers. Sometimes he is a hero. Often he is a clown who loves mischief. Sometimes his tricks backfire on him, as in this story. It is told by the Indians of northern California.

Once old man Coyote wanted to gather some pine nuts. He went to Saykalal, the little gray squirrel, and said, "I'd like to gather some pine nuts. How do you get them?"

Saykalal answered, "First, I look around until I find a tree with many new cones on it. Sometimes the crop fails. Then there are only a few old cones left on the tree. Don't bother with a tree that has just a few old cones left on it. Wait until you find a pine loaded with new cones."

"Yes, yes, I know all that," old man Coyote said with an impatient wave of his hand. "But how do you get the cones down?"

obsidian
(ob sid'ē ən)
hard, dark,
glassy rock that
is formed when
lava cools

"I run up the tree and cut off the cones with my teeth," said Gray Squirrel. "Then I run down to see where the cones fell."

"But I can't cut off the cones with my teeth," Coyote said grumpily.

"That's true, you can't," said Gray Squirrel. "You'll have to use your obsidian knife. When you have as many as you want, climb down and get the nuts out."

"You're not telling me the truth about the way you get the cones down," said the foolish Coyote. For he never believed anything that meant a little work.

"Yes, I am! Yes, I am!" cried Saykalal.

"I don't believe it!"

Saykalal didn't like this, so he decided he'd have some fun with the old man. "Well, since I can't fool you, I'll tell you the easiest way," he said.

"Yes! Yes!" cried Coyote. "Hurry up and tell me!"

"You climb a tree, go out backward on the limb with your face toward the tree trunk. Then take out your obsidian knife and cut off the limb where it joins the trunk. In this way you won't have to climb down again. You'll just ride down on a limb loaded with pine nuts."

"That's more like it!" cried Coyote as he hurried away. Soon he found a tall tree full of

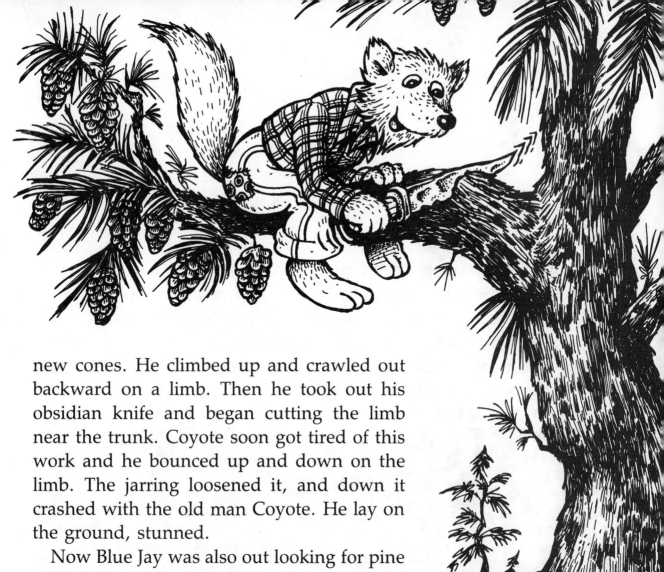

new cones. He climbed up and crawled out backward on a limb. Then he took out his obsidian knife and began cutting the limb near the trunk. Coyote soon got tired of this work and he bounced up and down on the limb. The jarring loosened it, and down it crashed with the old man Coyote. He lay on the ground, stunned.

Now Blue Jay was also out looking for pine nuts. He saw Coyote lying on the ground and flew down. He pecked on the old man's forehead, and cried in his piercing voice, "Wake up, Coyote, wake up!"

Coyote sat up and looked around. "I wasn't asleep," he growled. "Can't you let a great man lie in the shade and rest?" Then he picked himself up and sneaked off home. He didn't want to meet Saykalal, the little gray squirrel, just then.

Hooray for Hollywood!

At the start of the twentieth century, small theaters were opening up all over America. They were showing the wonder of Thomas Edison's invention—the moving picture. It cost only a nickel to see.

And so they called these theaters nickelodeons.

People were amazed to see people, animals, and machines moving on a screen. It is hard to imagine it now. But most people screamed and ducked when they saw a train that seemed to come out of the screen at them. They cheered for their heroes. They hissed at villains. They could

An early film-making crew

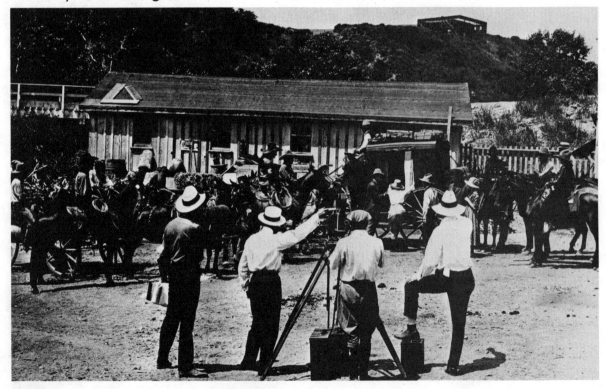

not believe it! And they could not get enough of it. They lined up in the streets to see the pictures that moved.

At first, almost all the movies shown in the nickelodeons were made in New York or Europe. (In those days movies were silent. So it did not matter if the actors spoke well or in a foreign language.) The only problem with making movies in New York was the weather. In the winter it was cold and the cameras froze. In the fall it was too cloudy. In the spring it rained a lot.

Where could the movie-makers make their movies where the weather was very good all year round? And where could they find cheap land for their studios?

Hollywood was a "sleepy" little town by the "sleepy" little city of Los Angeles. There was a lot of empty land. And land was cheap. The sun shone in winter, spring, summer, and fall. The climate was dry. And the natural scenery in the area was varied.

The moviemakers went west to California.

Hollywood became a dream of every American boy and girl. That was where stars were born. Americans read magazines that showed stars going to fancy nightclubs. They looked at pictures of stars stepping out of shiny cars that were longer than any cars today. And they dreamed of having their own mansions, their own furs, their own diamonds. They imagined themselves moving across the screen. They wanted to see their own names in glittering lights.

Fresh off the farms of the midwest, young Americans trailed to Hollywood. California in the 1920s was again the scene of a "gold rush." Here was a new generation, like the forty-niners before them, hoping to strike it rich. The movies promised them instant fame and fortune. Only this time riches were not to be found in mountains and riverbeds. Here dreams came true on the silver screen.

Of the thousands of hopefuls, only a few ever became famous and rich. Most of these young people got no closer to stardom than the front of Grauman's Chinese Theatre. (That is where the stars put their hand- and footprints in concrete.) For most of them, Hollywood was the land of broken dreams.

But new stories kept the old dreams alive. A new type of strike-it-rich legend was born in Hollywood. It was called "discovered in Hollywood." A "discovered" star was as good as gold. Lana Turner, it is claimed, was spotted at a local ice cream parlor. She was *discovered.*

In 1929, the Hollywood dream turned into a nightmare for many of the stars. Movies began to talk. And stars like Theda Bara, with her strong accent, and John Gilbert, with his high, squeaky voice, were no longer wanted. But new stars came to take their places. Thousands of Americans heard Al Jolson belt out "The Jazz Singer" on the screen.

The movies became more popular than ever. Every girl in America wanted a date with Cary Grant. Every boy wanted to be as

Film premiére at Mann's (formerly Grauman's) Chinese Theatre

Shirley Temple and Bill "Bojangles" Robinson

rugged and manly as Gary Cooper, Clark Gable, or Humphrey Bogart. Everyone wanted to dance like Fred Astaire or Ginger Rogers.

In the 1930s, jobs and money were hard to find. More people than ever went to the movies to forget their troubles. They laughed and cried with the faces on the screen. They watched Shirley Temple sing and dance her heart out with Bojangles. The movies became a habit. They have stayed that way ever since.

Hollywood—Believe It Or Not!

· A two-hour-long movie uses almost two miles of film.
· Electricity used to produce American movies for *one* day could light a town of 5,000 people for a year.
· The United States has about 13,000 indoor theaters and 3,800 drive-ins.
· An average movie costs as much as $25,000 a day to produce.
· Some movies scenes may cost as much as $25,000 an hour to shoot. These scenes may only last two minutes on the screen.
· As many as 44 million Americans see Hollywood movies every year.
· Over 130 million people in other countries see these films.

Today, American movies are still made in Hollywood. They also are made all over the world. But Hollywood is "miles" away from that quiet little town nestled outside Los Angeles at the turn of the century. It is the center of the music business and the television business. Its streets are crowded. Land is no longer cheap. Smoke from millions of cars often hides the famous California sun. But Hollywood will always be more than a town. Hollywood is the place where dreams are made. It is the place where stars do not just twinkle in the sky. They walk in the street.

"When I was nine I was the Demon King in *Cinderella* and it appears to have launched me on a long and happy life of being a monster."

—Boris Karloff

Pacific State Fare

ALASKA: "The Last Frontier;" "Land of the Midnight Sun"

State Motto: "North to the Future"

State Flower:
Forget-Me-Not

Main Industries:

Manufacturing: fish products, lumber and pulp, furs

Mining: gold, crude petroleum, natural gas, sand and gravel

Agriculture: oats, cabbage, turnips, barley, hay, sheep

Other: commercial fishing

State Tree:
Sitka Spruce

State Bird:
Willow Ptarmigan

OREGON: "The Beaver State"

State Motto: "The Union"

Main Industries:

Manufacturing: lumber and lumber products, food processing, transportation equipment

Mining: nickel, gravel and stone, clay, cement

Agriculture: wheat, oats, poultry, livestock, fruit and nuts

Other: commercial fishing

State Flower:
Oregon Grape

State Tree:
Douglas Fir

State Bird:
Western Meadowlark

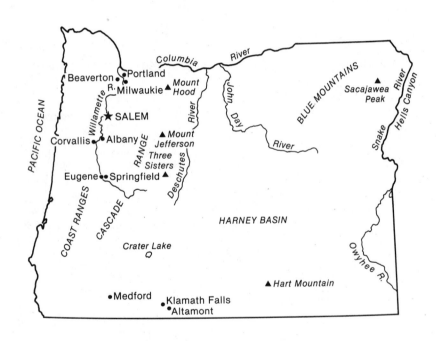

WASHINGTON: "The Evergreen State;" "Chinook State"

State Motto: *"Alki"* (Chinook word meaning Bye and Bye)

Main Industries:

Manufacturing: transportation equipment, lumbering, shipping, electronics, machinery, food processing
Mining: sand and gravel, stone
Agriculture: eggs, dairy products, wheat, apples, livestock
Other: commercial fishing

State Flower:
Coast Rhododendron

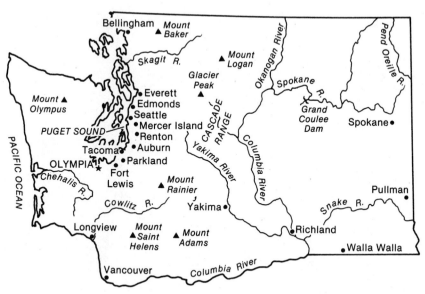

State Tree:
Western Hemlock

State Bird:
Willow Goldfinch

CALIFORNIA: "The Golden State"

CALIFORNIA REPUBLIC

State Motto: "Eureka"

Main Industries:
Manufacturing: aerospace, food processing, machinery and electrical equipment
Mining: petroleum, natural gas, boron
Agriculture: cotton, grapes, dairy, nuts, poultry, fruits, vegetables, grains, feed crops,
Other: tourism, commercial fishing

State Flower:
Golden Poppy

State Tree:
California Redwood

State Bird:
California Valley Quail

HAWAII: "The Aloha State"

State Motto: *"Ua mau ke ea o ka aina i ka pono."*
         (The life of the land is perpetuated in righteousness.)

Main Industries:
Tourism: "the visitor industry"
Manufacturing: sugar refining, pineapple canning, clothing
Agriculture: sugar, pineapple, flowers, macadamia nuts, coffee, beef cattle
Other: commercial fishing

State Flower:
Hibiscus

State Bird:
Nene (Hawaiian Goose)

State Tree:
Kukui

KAUAI Kapaa
Kekaha
Puuwai Waimea
NIIHAU

OAHU
Wahiawa
Pearl City Kaneohe
Waipahu Kailua
HONOLULU MOLOKAI
         Kalaupapa
Waikiki Kamakou
Beach Kaunakakai Lahaina MAUI
Lanai City Pukalani
LANAI Kahului Haleakala Crater

KAHOOLAWE

PACIFIC OCEAN

Honokaa
Mauna Kea Papaikou
HAWAII Hilo
Kailua Wailuku R.
Mauna Kilauea
Loa Crater
Pahala
Naalehu

Pacific States Sing-Along

Alaska's Flag
Eight stars of gold on a field of blue—
Alaska's flag. May it mean to you
The blue of the sea, the evening sky,
The mountain lakes, and the flow'rs nearby.

Words by Marie Drake   Music by Elinor Dusenbury

I Love You, California
I love you, California, you're the greatest state of all.
I love you in the winter, summer, spring and in the fall.
I love your fertile valleys; your dear mountains I adore.
I love your grand old ocean and I love her rugged shore.

Words by F. B. Silverwood   Music by A. F. Frankenstein

Hawaii Ponoi (Hawaii's Own True Sons)
Hawaii ponoi,   *Kamehameha e*
Nana i kou moi   *Na Kaua e pale*
Kalani Alii ke Alii   *Me ka ihe*
Makua lanie

Words by Kalakaua   Music by Henry Berger

Oregon, My Oregon
Land of the empire builders,   *Conquered and held by free men,*
Land of the golden west;   *Fairest and the best.*

Words by J. A. Buchanan   Music by Henry B. Murtagh

Washington, My Home
Washington, my home;   *This is my land, my native land,*
Wherever I may roam;   *Washington, my home.*

Words by Helen Davis   Music by Stuart Churchill

Excerpts from official state songs